The Great
Herb Compendium

Warning

This book is neither a manual for self diagnosis nor does the information contained herein claim to be comprehensive and/ authoritative. Herbs, seasonings and medicinal plants may have toxic effects. Neither the author nor the publishers shall liable or responsible in case of a plant's wrong application.

Photo Credits

AKG-photo, Berlin: pp. 9, 12, 13, 14; / Erich Lessing: p. 11; Archiv Fackelträger Verlag GmbH, Cologne: p. 4–6 (3), pp. 20 top le 22 (2), 23 centre, 69, 70, 72, 75, 76, 78 (2), 79, 83, 125; BilderKiste, Monika Zilliken, Hünstetten: /archive: pp. 11, 12 botto 36 bottom, 38 top, 62 bottom, 115 bottom, 120 bottom; /Monika Zilliken: pp. 10, 18, 19, 20 right, 21 (3), 23 top, 23 botto 50 top, 51, 54 top, 61 top, 68, 71, 73, 74, 116, 119, 122, 123, 124; dpa/picture alliance, Frankfurt: p. 17; PixelQuelle: p. 22, 6 Wolfgang Redeleit, Bienenbüttel: pp. 25, 26 bottom, 37, 40, 42, 44, 47, 48, 52, 54 bottom, 59, 60, 61 bottom (2), 62 top, 6 66, 69, 71, 74; Nils Reinhard, Heiligkreuzsteinach-Eiterbach: pp. 31, 39, 41 top, 43; Reinhard-Tierfoto, Heiligkreuzsteinac Eiterbach: pp. 7, 8, 15, 16, 24, 26 top, 27, 28 (2), 29, 30 (3), 36 top, 38 bottom, 41 bottom, 46, 49, 50 bottom, 55, 58, 68, 7 73, 111, 112, 114, 115 top, 117, 118, 120; TLC Fotostudio GmbH, Velen-Ramsdorf: pp. 80–82 (3), 84–110 (24)

Front cover images: From left to right: Archive NGV (1, 4, 5, 6, 7); getty images, Munich (2); dpa/picture alliance Gmb Frankfurt/Main (3)

Back cover images: From top to bottom: Interfoto (1, 3); dpa/picture alliance GmbH, Frankfurt/Main (4, 5); Archive NGV (

Illustrations: all Naumann & Göbel Verlagsgesellschaft mbH, Cologne (Marlene Passet in cooperation with Barbara Buccoli Lena Bückert, Saskia Erman, Moritz Gemke, Belinda Kramer, Florian Mitgutsch, Otto Mitgutsch and Eva Schrüßner) apa from: Beckhaus-Design, Peter Beckhaus, Mainz: pp. 32, 33, 34, 35

© Naumann & Göbel Verlagsgesellschaft mbH, a subsidiary of

VEMAG Verlags- und Medien Aktiengesellschaft, Cologne

www.vemag-medien.de

Author: Monika Zilliken; encyclopaedia part (pp. 125–156) in cooperation with Dr. Hans W. Kothe;

recipes pp. 80–110 Fackelträger Verlag GmbH, Cologne

Translation from German: Ingo Wagener, german-connection, Munich

Complete production: Naumann & Göbel Verlagsgesellschaft mbH, Cologne

Printed in China

All rights reserved

ISBN: 978-3-625-11443-7

The Great
Herb Compendium

FOR KITCHEN, HEALTH AND BEAUTY

TABLE OF CONTENTS

Herbal Culture 9

Growing Herbs 17

In the Kitchen 75

Home Medicine Chest and Cosmetics 111

A–Z of Herbs 125

Index 157

How to Use This Book

The "Great Herb Compendium" is a general introduction to the cultivation, care and propagation as well as different uses of herbs. While the information you will find listed in the book is thoroughly researched and double checked and as comprehensive and authoritative as possible, you should see it more as an introduction.

Handling Herbs Safely

Those who use herbs always (!) do so at their own risk. Neither the publisher nor the author can be aware of possible individual sensitivities or allergies nor the patient's general state of health. You must also be aware that some plants, if ingested or applied in larger amounts or over a longer period of time, may have toxic effects and can lead to poisoning.

We therefore warn expressively against and advise not to use or apply herbal medicines in a careless manner. This can include what may appear to be a harmless ointment or cream if the patient is allergic to any of its active ingredients. In order to avoid any problems and forego any possible risks, it is advisable that the patient – especially in the case of serious or chronic illnesses or ailments – does not do a self-diagnosis but always gets an appointment at the local GP or health centre.

Special care has to be taken when dealing with children, the elderly and pregnant women in administering or even considering to administer herbal medicines. Weight and the general state of health have also to be considered to find the right dosage of the plant in question. You really must consult your GP, if you have any doubts whatsoever about the treatment.

TOP TIP

Always collect wild herbs from environmentally sound spots to avoid contamination, and always wash thoroughly before usage.

Collecting Herbs

Mistakes can happen at any time, not only at the application phase. Collecting seasonings and medicinal herbs and preparing them is also an art in itself. It is ever so easy to mistake one medicinal herb for another if you are not 100% sure of its overall characteristics and habits. Moreover, there is always the danger of medicinal plants being contaminated in one way or other by fertilisers, insecticides or exhaust fume emissions. This is especially the case if the site is close to agricultural farm land or next to a street or busy road. Washing does not do any good in either case. But the forest and meadows are not entirely free of risks either. It is quite possible that the plant in question is infested with the fox tapeworm. The larvae of this pest are so small you will be hard pushed to even see them. Worse, they will damage your liver. How do they get there? If the wort has any contact with fox dung, it is quite possible for the larvae to wait there until ingested by another host. A good example is woodruff because it grows low on the ground. It is therefore wise to go to uncontaminated sites only and wash your gathered herbs thoroughly as soon as you get home. Freezing or drying herbs will not reduce the risk of contamination, only heating to more than 60 °C/140 °F will destroy any pests. Be also aware that some plants are protected species.

Herbs You Have Grown Yourself

You can avoid all of the above risks in a most appealing way – namely by growing your own herbs either in the garden, on the balcony or even the windowsill. This is the only way of knowing exactly the environment the plants have grown up in. You will also have total control over the usage, and if any, of possible fertilisers or insecticides.

In this book you will find a great deal of practice oriented tips as well as tried and tested advice on how to grow your own herbs successfully. It does not matter whether you have a garden or "only" a windowsill in your kitchen at your disposal. You will still be able to grow those herbs you need, so let yourself be guided by the suggestions listed in this book. You will be amazed at the manifold uses of herbs and worts and will surely enjoy many of the benefits they afford.

Use the great variety and diversity of herbs on offer – not only because you may be feeling a little off colour. Herbs will enrich your everyday life. Not only will they add a little something to your cooking but will benefit your digestive tract following a rich meal in the form of a tasty drink. A herbal bath will see you right after a strenuous day. Immerse yourself into the pleasant herbal aromas and treat yourself with, for example, home made facial tonics or perfumes. To use herbs only in case of ailments such as a cold or a runny nose would mean to waste many wonderful opportunities of how herbs could really improve your everyday life.

Herbal Culture

More Than the "Salt" of the Earth

These days we quite naturally regard herbs as seasonings and medicinal plants. They not only enrich our dishes with their aroma, but if taken in moderation, they are also quite capable of contributing to our well-being. Herbs have preventative and actual healing properties. We have a full range of different varieties at our disposal, some of which grow on the window sill, others out in the garden, while others again reach us ready packed from far fetched countries half way round the globe. In spite of this, it has taken a long time to reach the standard of knowledge about each and every herb and the richness of choice we enjoy today.

Trial and Error

Both primitive people and civilised cultures on all continents have been gathering local plants since time immemorial. Even if the first and foremost aim may have been to get food on the table, it was not long before peo-

ple came to notice the aroma and healing properties of some of these plants. It was probably more down to trial and error than exact science that people found out that meat seasoned with these plants was not only tastier, but also more easily digestible and induced a feeling of well-being. The same can most probably be said about these plants' healing properties. The observation of animals may well have helped the progress along the way, as they instinctively eat certain plants in case of ailments. No scientist can tell us today whether prehistoric man suffered fatalities because of this "trial and error" approach or whether intuitive action helped to alleviate certain afflictions. It has been proven, however, that herbs such as camomile, valerian, elder, plantain, yarrow (see left), flax, hemp and poppy must have been grown close to caves people used to live in.

"Primordial Herbs"

Evidence found in ancient tombs even points to certain plants which must have been held in high esteem by our ancestors. For example, graves at least 60,000 years old in both Mesopotamia and Egypt harboured remnants of medicinal herbs such as yarrow and marshmallow seeds, both of which are highly valued natural remedies to this day. First proof of our European ancestors using wild plants can be found at excavations of pile dwellings near Lake Constance (approximately 4,000 BC). During their work on these sites, archaeologists found remnants of poppies and caraway as well as the "forefather" of our parsley. What we do not know, however, is what dishes were graced by these herbs or for which ailments or illnesses they provided cures. Written records of exact application of a variety of herbs stem only from much more recent times. Knowledge of herbs and their uses have been passed on from generation to generation by nothing more than word of mouth for a very long time.

First Products of Herbal Cultures

Many of today's well-known herbs have their origins in far away tropical and sub-tropical regions. It was countries such as China, India, Egypt and Mesopotamia that were home to a lot of these plants. They were the first highly civilised cultures that developed writing systems; it is, therefore, not surprising that they also provided the first written records. Sumerian clay tablets from Mesopotamia which date back to the fourth millennium before Christ thus give us insights in the imports of plants and herbal recipes. One of these, dating back to 2,700 BC, describes a brown drug, "daughter of the corn poppy". The drug referred to was probably opium. At the same time, in China a written work detailing the healing properties of 365 plants was compiled during the regency of Emperor Sheng Nung, who is also considered the father of Chinese agriculture.

One of the oldest written records concerning healing properties of herbs stems from 3,000 BC and hails from Egypt. It even mentions that both cassia and thyme, amongst others, were used in the brewing of beer. One of the most informative texts, the Eber papyrus, also stems from Egypt. This 18 m/20 yard long scroll dates back to 1,500 BC and consists of 877 texts detailing mainly herbal recipes as well as the spells and invocations that went hand in hand with them in Egypt at the time. The scroll provides an insight into more than 80 plants and their dosage and lists more than 700 recipes including the making of medicines with herbs such as anise, cassia, fenugreek, fennel, calamus, cardamom, coriander, garlic, caraway, mint, poppy, saffron, mustard, sesame, thyme and wormwood. All of these herbs and worts are still highly valued today.

In India, too, the use of natural remedies was recorded round about the same time. The Veda, a collection of hymns whose title can loosely be translated as "Holy Knowledge", contains numerous details on the healing properties of certain plants. And the "Charaka Samhita", a collection of medicinal essays

Egypt can look back on a long tradition of herbs and seasonings.

taken down approximately 700 BC by the Indian physician Charaka, but whose origins supposedly go back much further, more than 1,500 plants are dealt with.

Ancient Herbal Knowledge

Round about the same time the civilisations of Europe and Asia tried to disassociate medical science from the world of magic, ghosts and spirits. After all, until then these superstitions had played an important part in the treatment of patients. Famous Greek and Roman scholars such as Hippocrates, Aristotle, Dioscorides and Galen were leading society away from these practices. Their writings built the foundations for the medicine we know today. Hippocrates (460-377 BC), probably most famous for the Hippocratic Oath, is seen as the father of medicine. The Hippocratic Corpus, or *Corpus hippocraticum*, describes some 230 medicinal plants. Even back then, Hippocrates was already looking for concrete causes of diseases and advocated the strict division between superstition and medical science. This revolutionary notion had a great impact on his immediate successors such as his fellow countryman Dioscorides, who lived in the 1st century AD and whose *De materia medica* lists some 800 medicinal herbs and Galen (approx. 129 – 199 AD), a Roman doctor of Greek origin, who composed hundreds of medical essays. Basically, they also influenced western medicine for the next one and half thousand years.

Dioscorides – author of the pharmacopoeia "De materia medica"

Herbs – the Rearguard of Roman Conquests

Apart from the obvious economical benefits of the conquest of both Egypt and Greece, the Romans also profited from their knowledge of medicinal plants of those cultures. Soon they learned to value the different herbs themselves. Indeed, herbs were held in such high esteem that the Roman armies carried them in their field packs all over Europe and Northern Africa and thus propagated the use and cultivation of these valuable aromatic and medicinal worts. It is estimated that the conquering Romans introduced more than 200 medicinal plants to the British Isles.

Monasteries –
Keepers of the Old Herbal Knowledge

Following the collapse of the Roman Empire, it was the Arabic medical tradition that not only kept alive the ancient knowledge but developed it further. The most noteworthy physician is probably Avicenna (980–1037), author of the famous encyclopedia *Canon medicinae* which was an indispensable reference and teaching book for any European physician until the 17th century.

In central Europe, however, it was mainly monasteries during the beginning of the Middle Ages who took it upon themselves to keep and develop medical knowledge. Although part of their efforts included the copying of old scriptures, they had special patches in their monastery gardens to grow herbs for both the nuns' and monks' own needs as well as for treating the local ill and unfortunate. Many monasteries therefore did not only boast a well stocked monastery garden with local and foreign plants but also functioned as special hospitals or infirmaries.

Worthy of a special note are the Benedictine monks. It was they who brought aromatic and medicinal plants, which they had a long tradition of growing in their monasteries, across the Alps and introduced them to Central Europe in the 9th century. Many other religious orders as well as Charles the Great (748–814 AD) benefited from the Benedictine monks, a fraternity founded 529 AD on Monte Cassino.

During his reign, Charlemagne decreed in his *Capitulare de villis* that worts and medicinal herbs should be paid greater attention to and grown more frequently throughout his lands. Indeed, he ordered that specific plants, 73 all in all, must be grown in every monastery in his kingdom. However, it did not end there. The decree included advice on how to gather, grow and keep numerous medicinal plants.

Dropping by the monastery's herbal garden was in olden days an everyday occurrence, similar to going to the chemist's today.

13

Medicinal Herbs During the Middle Ages

The Middle Ages saw the creation of a number of reference works on herbs, reflecting the great importance attached to these worts at the time. While the ancient Greek and Roman scholars had been busy separating medical science from superstition, magical powers once again made inroads into the medicine of the Middle Ages to form a nigh inseparable unit. Such learned men and women who spoke out openly against these mystic practices were usually thought of as magicians or witches by the Catholic church – and punished accordingly. Their abilities and knowledge consigned them to be burnt at the stake. The fact that the knowledge gathered over the millennia was not lost despite the terrible deeds of the inquisition is really down to nuns and monks. Protected by thick monastery walls and armed with both Latin and Greek, they were able to keep, develop and teach this knowledge. The oldest recorded monastery garden containing a medicinal herb patch dates back to 820 AD and was found in a Benedictine monastery in St. Gallen in Switzerland.

Hildegard of Bingen

While the books pertaining to herbs and worts used to be in Latin, the invention of printing by Johannes Gutenberg (1400–1468) saw written pieces relating to herbs and their usage reproduced in German and disseminated among the common folk. Because such books described both application and medicinal properties of these plants, they played an important part in establishing the first small herbal medicine cabinets.

Modern Medicine

Fortunately today the subject of medicinal herbs does not draw the same reaction as it used to back then. The danger of being burnt at the stake as a witch or magician is equivalent to zero. Older books on herbs by famous personalities such as the Abbess Hildegard of Bingen (1098–1179 AD, see left) have been rediscovered by popular medicine. But also modern medicine and the pharmaceutical industry would be nowhere near where they are today without the rich treasure of medicinal herbs at their disposal. These plants are also part of the foundations of naturopathic medicine – especially because of the lack of trust in pharmaceutical medicines and their often difficult to understand and numerous adverse effects. Many people are much more careful when it comes to using pharmaceutical drugs and are more likely to fall back on the old and proven natural remedies that their grandparents used and valued.

Herbs in the Kitchen

Herbs and worts probably found their way into the kitchen and pots and pans respectively at pretty much the same time as their medicinal properties were discovered. The first such cookbook was compiled by the Roman connoisseur Marc Anton Apicius in the 1st century AD. He reported of herbal mixtures that appear quite adventurous to our current tastes. Some of them, even if slightly changed, have survived and can be found in modern recipes, too. He also listed individual herbs such as lovage, oregano, coriander, caraway, dill, ginger, rue, mint, celery – and especially pepper. During the Middle Ages herbs were rarely used in the kitchen or for their aroma, not only because they were known to have medicinal qualities but also because they were frowned upon for having magical powers. It was only later that they were recognised to be excellent for adding that extra taste to certain dishes – usually through monks and nuns who were well versed in their usage. But it took the crusades and the subsequent contact with eastern cultures to reinstate herbs to their rightful place in the kitchen. Together with the newly gained knowledge, the imported herbs started a crusade of their own, mainly in the kitchens of the upper classes.

The ancient custom of using a lot of spices reached its peak during the Middle Ages. Not surprising if one considers the rather monotonous fare of the time. One would usually have a bowl of some or other very bland mushed cereal for breakfast, lunch and dinner. Aromatic herbs made it possible to add taste and do so very easily. However, creating different tasting food using these very expensive and usually imported ingredients from the East was to remain the privilege of the moneyed population. Those who could afford it would serve their guests dishes seasoned with spices and pepper, a good way to show off one's wealth and excellence of taste. The fact that digestion and appetite would also benefit was no more than a welcome side effect.

Not Without Herbs

Over the centuries the way people lived changed tremendously, a change also reflected in their eating habits. The improved economic situation following World War II brought affluence to large parts of the population and with it the once basic need for food changed to include certain culinary preferences and demands. Industrially processed food replaced good old fashioned cooking with its herbs and seasonings. For a long time only parsley or chives were used to add some flavour to salads and cooked dishes. However, since then the trend to go back to nature as well as the ecological movement have added renewed prominence to herbs in both gardens and kitchens. These days herbs once again take their rightful place in people's minds and good taste, a fact reflected by many scrumptious recipes.

The Ideal Role Model for the Herb Patch at Home – the Monastery Garden

Apart from the large scale vegetable gardens used to provide the monks or nuns with enough food throughout the year, religious orders also set up herb gardens close to the kitchens exclusively for tasty and wholesome worts. European monastery gardens varied from region to region. One thing most had in common, though, were the rigid geometrical forms, straight lines and beds full of typical plants lined with either wood or stones. The paths would usually meet in the centre of the gardens and sometimes be graced with a rondo. Over the course of time plants stemming mainly from the Mediterranean region were joined by native varieties to complete the monastery garden.

Ancestor of the Cottage Garden

Not before long, the inhabitants of medieval castles and palaces realised the benefits of having their own herb gardens. During these troubled times of battles and wars, herbs were used to treat ailments and injuries. It was from these castles, palaces and local monasteries that the common folk learned how to set up and run their own gardens. The rigid structure of monastery gardens was lost over time and apart from only vegetables and herbs, colourful flowers started being integrated to complete an aesthetically pleasing picture.

Examples of Your Own Herb Garden

Herb gardens of medieval monasteries continue to this day to be an excellent guide when it comes to composition and design. Naturally, the scale is quite different and cannot be adapted on a one-to-one basis, but if scaled down to suit one's own needs and climatic conditions, they form an excellent basis to start from. Cottage gardens are also ideal for learning about natural landscaping. Copying is the name of the game and you are most welcome to peek over the fence at your neighbour's garden or even visit a public herb or apothecary garden. Most are open until well into the autumn and free of charge.

An exemplary monastery garden is for example the historical herb garden of the German cloister Reichenau on Lake Constance.

Growing Herbs

When is a Wort a Wort?

Most people consider all plants which have some useful property or other to be a herb or a wort. Under this common definition, you will find everything ranging from seasonings to medicinal plants, fruit, vegetables but also plants of the onion family. The botanist, however, only counts those plants as herbs which are actually herb-like – that means they must have more or less green, soft, juicy and fleshy stalks and more often than not either die completely or only the root stock survives. Just a handful of worts can survive the cold season above ground. This group includes perennial bushes and those annual and biannual summer plants grown from seeds.

If we were to apply this definition, such plants as laurel, sage or rosemary, whose branches turn brown and

woody yet stay flexible even in young years, only to go completely woody later on would not count as herbs but bushes or shrubs. Of course, if you asked a chef, you would be told assuredly that you are dealing with herbs. We only have to think of "herbs Provençal" which are made up of such woody plants as basil, marjoram, tarragon, summer savory and chervil. This book goes along with current practices and traditions; therefore it includes all those plants that find their uses in medicine, cosmetics or even the new-fangled area of wellness. After all, each and every one has claimed their proper place in a well stocked herb garden.

A Wort, a Herb, a What?

Tradition has it that the countless varieties of herbs are subdivided in the following manner:

- seasonings – herbs which improve most dishes and even ease digestion because of their aromatic properties;
- medicinal plants – plants containing substances with therapeutic properties;
- wild herbs – plants which more often than not grow wild in nature, although some of them have made inroads into our gardens and may have manifold uses as seasonings, medicinal plants or even vegetables.

Which group which plant falls into is therefore largely dependent on the substances it contains.

Plant Substances

Why or how worts or herbs manage to not only improve the taste of a dish but at the same time possess healing properties was a closed book to our ancestors and often subject to much speculation – more often than not it remained a mystery. Chemical analyses and medical examinations have almost always supported old knowledge handed down through the ages. This does not mean, however, that each and every one of nature's agents has been sufficiently understood.

Quite often it is also the mixture of the herbal substances that create special properties, while isolated individual agents show no effects whatsoever. Most of these substances are actually by-products of the plant's own metabolism and can therefore belong to any one of the many families of chemical compounds. Below we list some of the most important of these substances.

Essential Oils

Essential oils are mostly intensely aromatic, volatile, oily metabolites produced and gathered in the plant's glands or special secretion cells respectively. Essential oils can be found in almost all parts of the plant be they flowers, leaves, needles, stalks, fruit, seeds, roots, wood or bark. They can either be a single ingredient or made up of a complicated recipe consisting of hundreds of different ingredients. These oils can have manifold effects on the human being. Some of them possess anti-inflammatory properties while others display antispasmodic, diuretic or even expectorant qualities to name but a few. Apart from that, there are also essential oils which, when applied externally, may slightly irritate the skin and thus improve blood circulation near the applied patches.

The most common method of extracting essential oils is by means of distillation. A typical plant containing an essential oil that has anti-inflammatory properties is for example camomile (Matricaria recutita, see left).

Because of its substances, common camomile is a much sought after and highly valued medicinal plant.

Left: summer savory (Satureja hortensis)
Right: flowering common rue (Ruta gravolens)

Bitter Constituents

Bitter constituents contained in herbs do not form a homogeneous group. Indeed, the only thing these very different substances share is their bitter taste. Plants use these bitter tasting constituents to defend themselves against their natural enemies. The therapeutic properties of bitter substances are based on the fact that they stimulate secretion of gastric juices as well as those of the gall bladder, thus improving both appetite and digestion. Some bitter constituents are also said to have tonic properties. There are many herbs which contain these bitter substances, among them yarrow (Achillea millefolium), common wormwood (Artemisia absinthium), mugwort (Artemisia vulgaris) or summer savory (Satureja hortensis).

Alkaloids

Alkaloids are relatively complicated nitric organic compounds especially prevalent in flowering plants. They gain their pharmaceutical properties from the present armino groups. Many very dangerous poisons are also alkaloids. If used in small dosage, they can be very effective medicines. In high dosages, however, they are addictive or deadly or both. A prime example is morphine which is extracted from poppies. Plants such as the valerian family as well common rue (Ruta graveolens) and comfrey (Symphytum officinale) contain relatively small amounts of alkaloids.

Tanning Agents

Tanning agents, also known under the names of tannin or tannic acid, are complex organic compounds that, to a greater or lesser degree, are present in nearly all plants. They are usually stored in either the bark or the plant's leaves, giving them an unpleasant taste – a reason why cattle for example avoid some plants. Tanning agents have the unique property of forming insoluble compounds together with the proteins of the body tissue (for example that of the skin or mucous membranes), thus contracting the tissue (astringent properties). These sub-

Top: lady's mantle (Alchemilla xanthochlora)

Centre: woodruff (Galium odoratum)

Bottom: marigold (Calendula officinalis)

stances are used in the manufacturing of leather. They have anti-inflammatory properties, reduce irritations and repress germs – all because they deprive the bacteria of much needed food for reproduction. Plants that are particularly rich in tanning agents include lady's mantle (Alchemilla xanthochlora), basil (Ocimum basilicum), sage (Salvia officinale) and comfrey (Symohytum officinale).

Glycosides

Glycosides in the plant kingdom are no rarity. These organic compounds often have quite different properties which is why they are subdivided into separate groups. The most important of these is probably that of the cardiac glycosides, substances that are used to increase the capacity of an otherwise not properly functioning heart. Moreover, they display diuretic properties which lead to a decrease of tissue liquids, thus lowering blood pressure. Cardiac glycosides are present in a number of different medicinal plants, the most well-known of which are probably the red foxglove (Digitalis purpurea) and woodruff (Galium odoratum). Diaphoretic glycosides are also well known from herbal teas, extracted from black elderberry flowers (Sambucus nigra).

Saponins

Saponins are a sub-group of herbal glycosides and belong to the family of phytosteroles. They consist of a sugar chain that dissolves in water and a fat soluble part termed genin. The name can be traced back to the fact that once dissolved in water, they form a stable soapy froth ("sapo" = soap). There are two distinct groups of saponins: triterpene saponins and steroid saponins. The latter share structural features with the steroid hormones of the human body; it is, therefore, not surprising that during treatment they may at times display hormonal activity. Triterpene saponins are

often powerful expectorants, i.e. substances that loosen secretions from the windpipe or the bronchial tubes. Steroid sapogenins are found for example in liquorice (Glycyrrhiza glabra); triterpene saponins amongst others in cowslip (Primula veris), marigold (Calendula officinalis), in small quantities in rosemary (Rosmarinus officinale) and even in the sweet violet (Viola odorata).

Phenols

Phenols are marked by their characteristic chemical structure in the shape of a ring. One of their most famous exponents is salycilic acid which forms the basis for the well know Aspirin®. Salycilic acid can, for example, be found in the white willow (Salix alba) and the sweet violet (Viola odorata). Another common phenol is thymol present in thyme (Thymus vulgaris). Phenols have a tradition of being used to disinfect wounds. If used in high dosages, however, they may irritate the skin to such an extent as to be harmful.

Flavonoids

The term flavonoids is a heading for a number of different agents that share the same chemical base structure. This group of mostly yellowish, nitrate-free phenolic compounds are extremely common in the plant kingdom. Their very different chemical and physical properties are reflected in the manifold possibilities of their medicinal uses. Their impact on the circulatory system is probably the most notable as is their effectiveness in case of cramps of the digestive tract or arteriosclerosis. Typical prepresentatives are wolf's bane (Arnica montana) which is often used in case of circulatory problems or ramson (Allium ursinum) in case of digestive disorders.

Mucilage

Many plants contain mucilage, an agent consisting of multi-chained sugar molecules that are water soluble and turn into a sticky, viscous mass. Their predominant therapeutic use lies in covering mucous membranes such as those of the digestive tract, thus protecting them from irritating or infectious agents. Mucilage can also be used, however, for its mild laxative qualities: its capacity to absorb water causes an increase of volume in the digestive tract. Another favourite use is to add it to bitter or strong tasting medicines, for it desensitises our taste buds. Plants containing a lot of mucilage include coltsfoot (Tussilago farfara), hollyhock (Alcea rosea), black elderberry flowers (Sambucus nigra), meadowsweet (Filipendula ulmaria), marigold (Calendula officinalis) or comfrey (Symphytum officinale). Water soluble mucilage has both anti-inflammatory as well as demulcent qualities.

Vitamins

Vitamins are absolutely essential substances to upkeep the human metabolism. Since our body is not capable of producing these itself, the only way of supplying it with vitamins is to ingest them. Fresh vegetables or herbs often contain lots of vitamins but the exact amount can vary greatly from plant to plant. For example, sorrel (Rumex acetosa), ramson (Allium ursinum), watercress (Lepidium sativum) and parsley (Petroselinum) all contain quite considerable amounts of vitamin C, while garlic (Allium sativum) boasts a whole cocktail of vitamins A, B1 and C.

Mineral Nutrients

Some herbs are very rich in mineral nutrients; that is, inorganic substances needed for the production of supportive tissue, the synthesis of enzymes and the functioning of the nervous system. Examples of plants rich in mineral nutrients are parsley (Petroselinum crispum var. crispum) and the stinging nettle (Urtica dioica) which contain a lot of iron; the dandelion (Taraxacum officinale) which can boast large amounts of calcium; and black elderberry flowers (Sambucus nigra), hops (Humulus lupoulus) and yarrow (Achillea millefolium) which are rich in potassium.

Top: hollyhock flower (Alcea rosea)

Centre: parsley (Petroselinum var. crispum)

Bottom: dandelion (Taraxacum officinalis)

A Good Plan is a Must

Prior to committing yourself to anything greater than buying a few pots of herbs for the kitchen windowsill, you should take stock of all the possibilities at your disposal. Check your garden, terrace, balcony, windowsills – how much space do you actually have, what are the light conditions like, what quality is your soil? Also take some time to think about what you want and need from your herb garden. Is the primary aim to supply the kitchen with fresh herbs? Are you more interested in medicinal plants or are you after a place that will calm you down every time you spend some time there? Or is it a mixture of all three? Most important of all, how much time do you want to and are able to spend on building it and keeping it up?

Bearing in mind all these considerations you should take another look at your garden, your terrace or the balcony. Every single one of these components has a direct impact on the design and development of your herb garden. From the traditional, strictly geometric arrangement of plants as we know from medieval monastery or apothecary gardens, all the way to the organic cottage gardens where you will find carrots growing in perfect unity with kitchen herbs, both complementing the neighbouring hollyhocks towering above them. These are the extremes of the spectrum, giving you plenty of space in between to let your creativity, fantasy and individual taste free reign. Regardless of which direction your fancy takes you, the following tips should always be borne in mind:

Sun, Sun, Sun... and Poor Soil

Most herbs used as seasonings or as medicinal plants stem from the Mediterranean and are therefore accustomed to real sun. It is not surprising that they can only attain their full aroma and height when they get enough light and warmth and are protected from cold draughts. Despite this, they are not fussy when it comes to soil. On the contrary, they are particularly fond of poor and permeable soils. Naturally, exceptions only go to prove this golden rule. Many of Central Europe's native plants such as chives, veronica, peppermint or woodruff prefer moister and richer soils.

Position it Close to the House

Herbs for seasoning or medicinal plants are mainly used in the kitchen or at least that is where they are usually prepared. If the site allows it, they should thus always be grown close to the kitchen to avoid muddy feet later on.

Water

Herbs simply love stale and soft water. It would therefore be a good idea to have a rain barrel close by. And while you are at it, you might want to consider a bird bath or something smaller for insects, as many herbs are rich pastures for bees, bumblebees and butterflies.

Decorative Materials

Beds have to have borders, paths need foundations and drainage and you might even consider some fencing. Always use simple materials such as natural stone, wood, wattle, ceramics or clay. All of these harmonise with the idea of having a natural herb garden.

Combine natural materials such as quarry stones or round timber to border a herb bed.

Proper Design

Light and soil conditions are among the most important factors when it comes to a successful herb garden and, of course, to the right selection of herbs. The table on pages 56 and 57 as well as the listed characteristics at the back of the book from page 125 to page 156 will provide you with relevant information. Once you have identified suitable plants, your own requirements and wishes can be taken into consideration to reach a final selection.

Classical and Formal

These small "gardens" within a garden purposely imitate the tradition of old monastery gardens. A clear layout of paths out of bricks, clinkers or pebbles determine both structure and geometry of the entire site. But that is not their only purpose. They also afford easy access to all plants and herbs in their vicinity. In the centre of the garden we usually find some ornament or other such as a sculpture, a large plant pot or even a decorative climbing rose.

The classical boxwood (Buxus sempervirens 'Suffruticosa') is often used as a border for beds. More interesting and varied are of course borders made out of woody aromatic herbs. There is, however, a small disadvantage to the latter solution: they have to be kept in shape through regular cutting and the plants will have to be replaced every few years or as soon as they become leggy. If one thinks ahead and takes cuttings (please refer to page 60) in good time, however, even this seemingly annoying problem become little more than a minor inconvenience.

Carefully separated beds afford each wort its own home (above) – below the somewhat more carefree and modern interpretation.

The Cottage Garden

The cottage garden is the less formal yet legitimate successor of the monastery gardens. Although the term cottage garden refers to a wide variety of different designs, we will take it to mean mostly gardens divided by hedges or boxwood. The cottage garden is home to all those plants not hardy enough to survive in the open field and those which are needed close to home for daily use. Early cottage gardens were therefore home to many herbs, vegetables and the odd medicinal plant. Throughout time, a number of additions were made that to this day experience continuous refinement through special breeding. Thus flowering plants like hollyhocks, delphiniums, marigold, peony and Turk's cap lilly started to grace these patches of green and were enjoyed by people and animals alike.

The cottage garden is a beautiful example of mixed cultivation. Annual herbs grow right next to vegetables. Glorious flowering plants neighbour onto perennial herbs and worts used as seasonings. There is a distinct advantage to this kind of cultivation: the constituents of most herbs, the odd vegetable or even bushes permeate into the ground and have beneficial effects on their neighbours. At times these agents can even keep pests at bay (please also refer to pages 52 to 54 for plant protection). This is a form of symbiosis and biological pest control that does not involve any additional labour. To have a colourful cottage garden is therefore not yielding to antiquated nostalgia but one of the most up-to-date ways to combat pests in a biologically sensible manner.

Traditionally the cottage garden is home to vegetables, herbs and flowering plants.

A central path or paths arranged in the form of a cross made of pebbles or some wooden surface serve to organise a garden. Another favourite surface is bark mulch as it blends in perfectly with its natural surroundings. The centre may be occupied by a rose climbing up a gazebo with a bench in the middle where you can spend some quality time.

Once again it is boxwood that forms the traditional border. Just as suitable, however, is densely planted parsley, field salad or low growing flowering plants such as French marigold or carnations (especially carthusian pink). But perhaps you prefer to border your beds with the aromatic wild thyme.

The Economical and Low Maintenance Solution – the Square

Convenient and practical, this form is reminiscent of a classical vegetable garden. Irregularly laid stepping stones or straight paths dissecting the individual beds – covered with either mulch or pebbles or even timber – make for easy access and enable a comfortable working environment. If the bed can be reached from one side only it should not be wider than 80 cm/2 ½ feet, twice as wide if there is a path on either side of it.

Take care when planting out your herbs of choice: place the lower ones in front and taller ones such as lovage or tarragon further to the back so that they do not prevent light from reaching all the plants. Attractive colourful patches are provided by borders out of flowering plants. You should take care, however, that these do not grow too tall and prevent easy access to your valuable herbs.

If care is taken with the positioning of plants, all will thrive on the available light (here thyme at the front, French lavender in the centre and the curry plant at the back).

Effective and Geometrical – the Cartwheel

Few people can boast of a garden that has enough space for a large scale herbal rondo so prevalent in old apothecary gardens. In this case a different solution is called for. A trip to the local farmer or antique shop may well provide you with what you were looking for: an old wooden cartwheel. Simply plant the herbs in between the spokes and you have natural borders and an already organised pattern. In order for the general shape and pattern provided by the wheel to stay recognisable throughout the whole year you will have to cut back and harvest quite rigorously. This holds especially true for the late summer. However, the rule of tall plants to the back and smaller ones to the front does not work one to one for a cartwheel. We just have to adapt it slightly and plant all taller herbs towards the middle of the wheel, while the smaller ones are positioned closer to the rim. This way every plant should be quite happy where it is.

An attractive attention getter in every garden: the herbal cartwheel.

TOP TIP

Raising your herbal bed a little not only makes for a very attractive feature, but you will also find that your back will be grateful for the easy access.

A Comfortable Height

A raised bed or, even preferable, an attractive herb mound puts a stop to the back breaking work and will grace every garden. Raised beds or mounds are no strangers to vegetable gardens and are usually made of a wooden frame of some 30 to 40 cm/1 foot to 1 foot 4 inches in height. Materials used vary from natural stone, round timber, planks, railway sleepers or whatever suits your taste.

Basically both the raised bed and the mount are nothing else but a compost heap with plants on top: The bottom layer consists of roughly chopped branches and other woody parts of plants. This is topped with a 10 to 15 cm/ 4 to 6 inches thick layer of fresh compost or manure followed by some 20 cm/8 inches of moist leaves covered with normal soil. The top 10 to 15 cm/4 to 6 inches thick humus layer is mixed with finished compost. Two noteworthy points particular to raised beds and mounds: first, the bed should slope down towards the sides so that water can run off unhindered. Second, you will need a small watering trench for the water not simply to disappear down the sides without reaching the plants' roots. Small plastic tubes inserted into the bed with a diameter of 3 to 4 cm/ 1 to 1 ½ inches and a length of nearly 10 cm/4 inches provide a handy solution to these problems.

Left: a herbal spiral out of natural stones is being filled with top soil.
Right: the same herbal spiral including plants.

Curl up in the Garden – the Herb Spiral

This particular kind of bed got its lease of life from the permaculture movement. Its structure is made out of natural stones which are arranged in such way as to form a spiral that is steadily increasing in height. Note that no mortar is necessary to keep the structure upright as the soil provides it with the necessary solidity. Using special foil, it is common to place a mini pond at the spiral's foot to accommodate those herbs that require a moist environment. If you decide against the pond, you should at least use very rich, moist topsoil for the lower part of the spiral. This will ensure that even peppermint, lemon balm or chives will feel at home. The rest of the spiral can be filled with regular soil. The top third should receive some sort of drainage in the form of pebbles or gravel to provide a sufficiently dry enough environment suitable for those well loved southern varieties like thyme, oregano or sage.

It is very important that the spiral is not too tightly wound – it should have a minimum diameter of 2 to 3 m/7 to 10 feet – to provide the herbs with enough space to develop properly and make an impact. You can easily add some nice spots of colour by allowing flowering herbs such as borage, yarrow, lady's mantle, marigold or even nasturtiums to join their non-flowering companions.

This setup enables herbs from a variety of different environments to be grown adjacent to each other.

A Small Miracle – the Herbaceous Corner

Not enough space for a "proper" bed? Rather have ordered "chaos" and a mixed and colourful topsy-turvy? In that case, you may want to consider the herbaceous corner. It is undeniable that such "uncontrolled" growth has a certain charm and appeal and insects will simply love the aromatic jungle. But once again, the herbs will have to be shown who is boss if they are to survive and get on well in such confined surroundings. The old rule holds, taller plants at the back, smaller ones to the front. Annuals and biannuals should also be placed in the front row so that timely replacements will not pose any problems. Regular trimming is of course a must in order to keep some sort of control and – even more importantly – to keep them healthy. Separate individual sections by means of stepping stones or pebbles and do not let spreading plants (peppermint, lemon balm) get out of hand by introducing proper borders to the bed. In order to give everything the final touch you might want to consider planting a colourful array of flowering plants around your herbaceous border.

On Aromatic Paths

Paved paths or just a row of slabs introduce enormous charm to the garden, especially if they can boast aromatic herbs along their edges. Low growing thyme is available in a number of different varieties as is Roman chamomile (Chamaemelum nobile), oregano or lavender. Any of these plants are perfectly happy even if planted in the smallest gaps alongside your paths.

Ever thought of an aromatic lawn, i.e. one that gives off a lovely smell as soon as one steps on it? What at first sight may seem an extravagance can be accomplished with the following plants: citrus thyme, lavender-thyme, creeping thyme, the already mentioned Roman chamomile, pineapple weed which may produce wonderful flowers but provides a thick, soft cover. All of the above are not fussy and can stand anything from sun to partialshade. For each square metre of aromatic lawn, you will require some 5 to 7 plants which you should plant out in the autumn so that you can enjoy the full

TOP TIP

An attractive alternative to natural stone slabs is natural wood, in this case discs of tree trunks surrounded by aromatic herbs.

glory of your new acquisition the following year. You will have to get rid of weeds until the area is fully covered by the herbs. Wait with the lawn mower until the plants are properly established, and use garden shears until then. Be careful – do not walk barefoot on thyme as it is the perfect playground for bees and bumblebees.

Some Planting Schemes – Themed Beds

Once the idea has taken seed, it is hard to stop it. It is a surprisingly small step from a selection of potted herbs to a full blown herb garden. On the following pages we will introduce four different planting schemes. Use them as they are or see them as suggestions to help you design your own aromatic patch.

Family Bed

4 x 3 m/13 x 10 feet is about the right size for a herb bed in order to supply a family of four with a sufficient amount of herbs. The planting scheme below should satisfy all tastes and includes not only typical herbs for the kitchen, but also medicinal plants as grown and used in the old monastery gardens.

1 lovage	9 sage	17 lemon thyme	25 nasturtium
2 wormwood	10 apple mint	18 thyme	26 marjoram
3 tarragon	11 lemon balm	19 burnet saxifrage	27 chervil
4 mugwort	12 hyssop	20 rue	28 parsley
5 lavender	13 borage	21 southernwood	29 watercress
6 fennel	14 garden sorrel	22 winter savory	30 chives
7 rosemary	15 peppermint	23 summer savory	31 garlic
8 dill	16 oregano	24 basil	32 onions

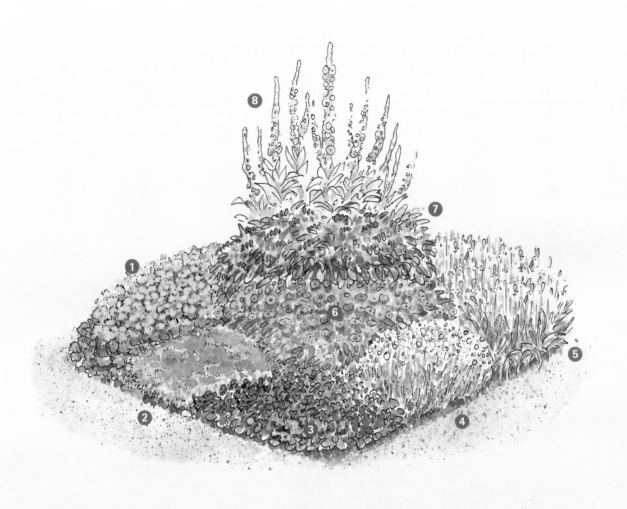

"Apothecary" Bed

Blessed are those who can boast their own first aid garden – regardless of its size. Old traditional remedies will help you with coughs, colds, a sore throat, bee stings, an upset stomach, headaches... There is a wort against them all.

1 lady's mantle (Alchemilla xanthochlora)

2 thyme (Thymus vulgaris)

3 sweet violet (Viola odorata)

4 German chamomile (Matricaria recutita)

5 ribwort plantain (Plantago lanceolata)

6 marigold (Calendula officinalis)

7 comfrey (Symphytum officinalis)

8 common mullein (Verbascum densiflorum)

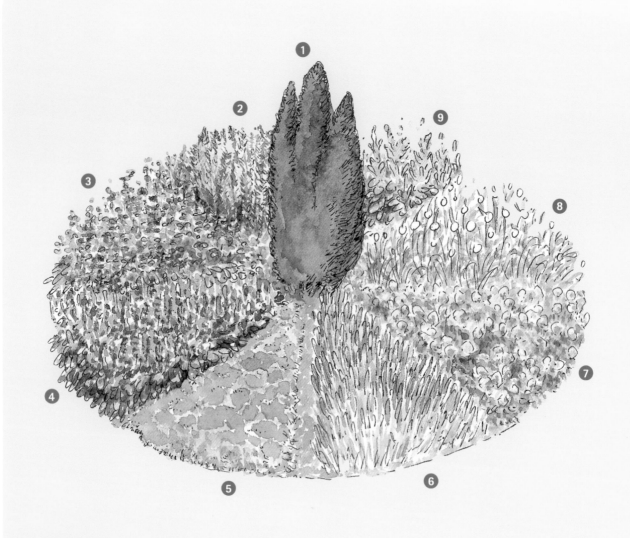

Mediterranean Aroma

A collection of favourite herbs from the Mediterranean is an absolute must if you are a fan of the Italian or Mediterranean cuisine. There is nothing like having these taste boosters fresh on your doorstep. Not only will they improve your cooking, but they will also be a welcome distraction for both eyes and nose. If the Mediterranean bed is planted in a round shape, it becomes a real eye-catcher.

1 juniper (Juniperus communis)

2 rosemary (Rosmarinus officinalis)

3 sage (Salvia officinalis)

4 basil (Ocimum basilicum 'Rubin')

5 thyme (Thymus vulgaris)

6 lavender (Lavandula angustifolia)

7 oregano (Origanum vulgare)

8 garlic (Allium schoenoprasum)

9 clary (Salvia sclarea)

The Relaxing Aromatic Island

Stressed, washed-out, tired? Use nature's little helpers in the form of aromas that will pick you up again. Herbs are your friends. Already a small corner in your garden will suffice to provide you with those herbs that are necessary to banish the problems of everyday life.

1 multiflora rose (Rosa multiflora)

2 rosemary (Rosmarinus officinalis)

3 peppermint (Mentha x piperita)

4 lemon thyme (Thymus citriodorus)

5 lavender (Lavandula angustifolia)

6 German chamomile (Matricaria recutita)

7 lemon balm (Melissa officinalis)

The Mobile Herb Garden

Herbs in tubs, boxes, bowls and bell pots are not only a treat for the eyes – they are also the ideal solution to the problems posed by a small garden or if you are confined to a terrace, balcony or only a windowsill. Pots and containers that are somewhat out of the ordinary can supply your garden or your balcony with a southern flair you would not have thought possible. Nearly all herbs can be grown in containers and an array of different troughs, pots, urns and containers will make all the difference. Combine tall with small ones, arrange plants with the help of tiered shelving, steps, bricks or clinkers on a number of different levels – this not only looks pretty but provides each and every plant with enough fresh air and light to grow and thrive. Smaller containers can be attached to walls and plants such as nasturtiums can be accommodated in attractive hanging baskets.

The Right Choice of Container

You can basically use any old container you see fit as long as it does not contain any harmful substances. The only proviso is that it must have drainage holes. You may as well let your fantasy free reign: regardless of whether you keep to the traditional clay and terracotta pots, troughs made of wood, granite containers, special pots with planter holes (see page 37) or unusual plastic planters – everything is allowed as long as the plant is happy in it. This method has saved more than one container from an untimely end on the dump and given it a new lease of life. The only material that is not suitable as a plant container is metal.

Apart from the drainage, holes mentioned above you should really have an additional drainage layer at the bottom of your containers. Simply cover the drainage holes with pieces of broken clay pots and fill the container with a mixture of sand and gravel approximately 1 to 2 cm/½ to 1 inch thick. Now even large amounts of water can drain off without the danger of standing water that will rot your herbs. Remember that especially Mediterranean herbs are used to warm and well drained soil and cannot stand wet feet.

Among the bewildering choice of different containers, you will also have to consider their size. If in doubt, always go for the bigger one. This is especially true if you are thinking of planting perennial, tall or spreading herbs such as laurel, sage, lavender or rosemary. Creeping herbs like all kinds of mint, lemon balm, tarragon or those that develop deep root systems such as lovage not only prefer a larger home but will thank you in later life if each has their own pot or container.

The same is of course true of the classical flower boxes. These, too, require proper drainage so that your plants can thrive. If possible choose the larger ones of a metre/3 ½ feet in length to give enough space for about eight plants.

Soils and Substrates

Most aromatic herbs and medicinal plants count among the less fussy specimen of the plant kingdom. One thing to bear in mind, however, is that you can only add certain amounts of soil to a pot – naturally the same is true of the nutrients contained in that soil. Despite this, a mixture made up of normal soil composts available from your local garden cen-

Such attractive terracotta pots – note the extra planting pockets – provide a maximum of herbs in a minimum amount of space.

tre should be perfectly adequate. Alternatively mix together some fresh compost, bark mulch and a little sand. If you really want to treat your plants, you can add bone meal or other long term fertiliser and your annual and biannual plants should be happy for life. Any other forms of fertilisation are usually not necessary. Perennials will benefit greatly if repotted annually and, if necessary, moved to a larger size container or pot. If the plant's leaves turn yellow – amongst others a sign of undernourishment – you should repot the plant in a pot filled with fresh soil so that it can recover. Take good care when using very peaty compounds as they tend to dry out very quickly – frequent but little water is the answer to this particular problem.

Water is a Must

While the supply of nutrients is naturally important, it takes a clear second when it comes to watering your plants. Sun and wind dry out the comparably small amounts of soil rather quickly. Unfortunately, there is not really a one-fits-all solution to this problem: do the "finger test" and go along with the results. If the soil feels dry, water your plant; if it is still moist, wait a little longer. Should the soil be quite wet, leave it to dry out for a day or two. Especially Mediterranean herbs require less water than those native to our shores and used to our constant supply of water. In practical terms, this means that summer savor, for example, prefers dry conditions while dill loves it to be moist but not wet. Perennials require less moisture during autumn and winter. This is not surprising since this is their resting period.

A Question of Positioning

Probably the most important aspect when it comes to whether your herbs will thrive in the minimum amount of space afforded to them is the site they stand on. While the garden has a number of different spots to choose from, there is less choice when looking for the correct lighting conditions on a terrace or balcony. More or less ideal are morning and afternoon sun, i.e. an east or a west facing position. This provides sufficient light and warmth for example for basil, summer savory, sage, thyme, wormwood and hyssop. Plants requiring less sun include watercress, lavender, lovage, lemon balm, mint and chives.

- If you have a southern facing spot you have it made. Many of the most popular aromatic herbs are Mediterranean in origin and cannot get enough sun. The following belong to the true sun-worshippers: summer savory, the curry plant, lavender, oregano, rosemary, sage, thyme and hyssop. But be careful, just because they love the sun does not mean they can survive a serious drought: do not forget to water them frequently.

With the wall protecting the herbs from wind and supplying them with heat stored during the day these plants will thrive.

• Much more difficult but by no means impossible is a northern facing spot. Ramson, borage, chervil, peppermint and even parsley will manage quite well if subjected to such poor lighting conditions.

Most of the time, however, we have a mixture of the above. This requires expertise and experience that can only be gained with time. It may be quite possible that basil thrives on your south to southwest facing plot while your neighbour with his south facing terrace cannot get it to grow at all.

Watering, too, is an art that will need practising because whichever way you are facing will influence the amount of water needed. Full sun will dry out soil in terracotta pots very quickly while continued shade on the north side may mean water clogged plants. Draughty spots, high-up balconies and other exposed sites will be subject to increased water loss meaning you will have to water your plants more frequently. Special care should be taken when dealing with hanging baskets as these are likely to dry out relatively quickly (see below).

Care and Sowing Out

All in all, herbs have retained most of the characteristics of wild plants; therefore, they do not require any additional care. If both site and watering are fine, there really should be very little that can go awry. Even fertilisation is hardly ever necessary. Pests such as aphids et al are also relatively rare as the plants can boast natural protection systems against anything untoward. If despite everything, you should come across a problem, the same rules apply for both pot plants and those grown in the garden (please refer to pages 52 to 54).

The same rules apply to sowing out as to the outdoors in general: you can easily sow out annual and biannual seeds yourself. Delicate plants should be raised indoors or in a growing frame first, while the more robust varieties do not have to undergo this strenuous journey and can be grown on their intended site. If the plants are too dense, you will have to thin accordingly. You can even grow perennials from seed

TOP TIP *It is best to give your plants water that has been left standing overnight. They will repay you soon enough.*

– but it requires a little bit of patience until the first harvest. Obviously you can pluck a leaf or two after the first year – this will also prove beneficial to the plant as a certain amount of trimming will keep it both in shape and healthy at the same time.

TOP TIP

Water frequently but little during the winter months. Most plants grown on the balcony do not freeze to death but die of thirst!

Protection During the Cold Season

As soon as the winter comes, it is a good idea to move all annual and biannual herbs inside into the warmth. Most perennials are hardy and may stay outside. However, care still has to be exercised: typical Mediterranean herbs may survive if exposed to such low temperatures as 0 °C/32 °F – but the only way to make sure of it is to move them inside during the cold season with the ideal site being a light and bright place with a temperature between 6 to 10 °C/43 to 50 °F. Those that will benefit from being moved indoors include French lavender, laurel and rosemary – as long as the latter is not a specially hardy sort that will survive outside.

Cut the herbs back by a third prior to moving them into the winter quarters. In any case, shorten extra long shoots. Control all plants for pests, remove if necessary and do not forget to water your herbs every now and then. It is imperative that the roots do not get starved of water. A little bit of instinct and expertise and, of course, growing experience will see you and your herbs safely through the cold winter months.

All hardy plants may stay outside. But these, too, do not scoff at a protected, dry site and a warming cover of branches or mulch. In the unlikely event that temperatures drop well below freezing for a longer period of time, you really should find the most protected spot in the garden and huddle them together. They will also be very grateful if they get wrapped up in a thick protecting layer of newspaper, sacking material or foil to prevent the soil from freezing. Another good idea is a 2 cm/1 inch thick layer of polystyrene on which to stand them so as to prevent the cold from creeping up into the pot. Remember: the smaller the pot the greater the likelihood of frost bite.

Playing Around with Colours and Forms

Of course there is nothing to be said against growing herbs and nothing but herbs on either balcony or terrace, but you will be surprised at some of the magical combinations that can be achieved by adding some flowers here or there. And that is true for both eyes and nose! So do not be afraid of what at first may sound like rather adventurous combinations. Parsley, peppermint or dill provide for an attractive structure amidst the green. Add some colour in the form of variegated basil or thyme or use the silvery wormwood, lavender or sage in coordination with colourful petunias or even the old time favourite geraniums.

One thing to bear in mind when trying different combinations are soil and site requirements of the plants in question. If they are too different from each other, your wonderful arrangement may not last very long. Another thing to watch out for is that some herbs like each other, while others cannot stand certain neighbours. Thus borage and parsley or rocket salad is a recipe for disaster as is putting basil next to dill, marjoram or oregano. The same goes for the combination of peppermint and lemon balm while thyme cannot bear to be in the same pot as oregano or marjoram. However, if each has their own container the experiment should work.

It may be shady, but not in the least bit boring: borage, veronica, celery, parsley and a few daisies in between to add some extra colour.

A raised bed on the edge of a terrace provides space for attractive plants such as herbs, flowering plants and even tomatoes.

Tasty Titbits From the Windowsill

You do not have to forego the pleasure of a herb garden even if you do not have a terrace or a balcony or let alone a garden. There is enough space virtually anywhere for a bright, airy spot in the sun, namely a windowsill. You can grow more or less all herbs indoors. The only ones to pose problems might be the tall lovage, fennel, mugwort, rue or wormwood. However, you cannot expect your herbs to reach the same size as those grown outside. The small plant pots and conditions which are not as ideal as those only nature can provide do take their toll. Look on the bright side and consider your herbs to be "bonsai" varieties. So what, who would want to miss that aroma? You will be grateful for your mini garden sooner than you know it but at the latest when the days grow shorter...

Room with a view: bright, airy and the ideal temperature – this combination will ensure that your herbs will thrive even on a windowsill.

Bright, Warm – But no Draughts, Please

Nearly all advice given in the previous chapter "The Mobile Herb Garden" is also valid for growing your herbs indoors. Provide as much light as possible – but be careful! While a south facing windowsill may be perfect in the winter, even lovers of the sun such as rosemary or thyme cannot cope with the bright midday sun. You will need to provide shade during those hours. You may ask why? Well, the window acts much like a lens would burning your precious herbs. An ideal site is a bright east or west facing windowsill. This can only be topped by a proper conservatory.

Herbs hate large differences of temperature. It is therefore not surprising that they rebel and even give up their ghost entirely if placed above radiators or in the direct line of serious draughts. For this reason, the bedroom may be a more favourable site than the kitchen. As with everything, you will have to gain experience to see where your herbs are happier. Also consider what to do when larger herbs are moved inside during the cold winter months. To reduce the stress of moving, you should ensure that the differences in temperature remain manageable. If this is not possible, you may want to get them used to the changed conditions step by step.

Fresh Air is a Winner

Fresh air is an absolute necessity – this is true of all plants which are kept in buildings. No plant can survive without a decent circulation of air around it. It is therefore wise not to crowd the pots together even though this might be more pleasing on the eyes. Remember, fresh air is absolutely vital. Afford those herbs that "live" in your flat or house a trip into the fresh air, even if this is only the other side of the windowsill and do so as often as possible. The pots will obviously have to be secured so that they do not fall off. A viable alternative is to keep the window open for as long as possible, but once again be careful of those dangerous draughts.

All About Pots and Containers

Which pots and containers are suitable depends on the width of your windowsill on the one hand and perhaps on the general style of the furniture in your flat or house on the other. But the most important thing to bear in mind are the needs of the plants themselves. Drainage is once again vital. As stated before, shards of broken pots to cover the drainage hole combined with a thin layer of sand and gravel are a must before adding soil. An idea for those extra careful ones is to fill a tray with a thin layer of expanded clay on which to place the pot. This will make it nearly impossible for your precious herbs to get those dreaded "wet feet" and rot from the base upward.

Less is More

Normal compost available from your local garden centre contains too many nutrients for your undemanding herbs and you will have to "thin" it with some sand or fine gravel. This prevents the threat of pending salination of your soil and creates an appropriate environment for your plants. Watering, too, is best done sparingly. The plants will quite happily survive a short drought while those much talked about "wet feed" would be life threatening. How frequently you should water your plants is dependent on the predominant room temperature and humidity. The best way of making sure is the traditional "finger testing" method: if the upper 1 cm/½ inch of soil is dry, your plants will thank you for a bit to drink. Many herbs and especially large leaved varieties such as basil or sage are also quite partial to a shower of tiny droplets of tepid water applied with a mister. Please note that it should only be used for this purpose and not for spraying any chemicals!

TOP TIP

Your windowsill inhabitants will be grateful for every bit of fresh air afforded to them.

You do not need to fertilise your herbs as normal compost contains more than enough nutrients. In any case, it should be more than enough for your annual plants. However, if you do notice yellow discolourations or in case harvested shoots only grow back feebly or not at all, you might be well advised to carefully add a few drops of fertiliser. Perennials should be moved to a larger pot and afforded fresh soil on an annual basis. During winter and the resting period, no fertiliser should be applied because the plants' metabolism literally slows down and the extra nutrients would only serve to confuse, if not harm them.

Vitamins on the windowsill: herbs will grow indoors, too, and will even provide a steady supply of fresh leaves throughout the winter months.

How Much Can I Harvest?

While life on the windowsill may not be all that bad, it is not comparable to that out in the open. As a consequence, herbs grown indoors will not be as robust and hardy as their counterparts which are looked after by mother nature. The same goes for those plants that are moved indoors during the cold winter months. You should therefore harvest with due care. Avoid removing the main shoots at all costs and take care not to cut too much of a shoot at any one time. Also, be careful and start harvesting at the bottom working your way to the top. This way you remove the older leaves first, never the young ones. While a frequent harvest and cutting back can improve an outdoor plant, it may well be the death of one indoors. One more thing to look out for is to prevent your indoor herbs from flowering. It may be pretty on the eye, but the plant will virtually waste all its strength to produce flowers possibly followed by seeds and will not have enough strength left to grow leaves, which is what you are after.

Treatment of Indoor Ailments

Unfortunately, those plants grown indoors are more prone to pests and common ailments than their counterparts grown outdoors. Aphids are often caused by soil which is too moist, thrips by dry air. If your plant has been infested, there is one thing you must not use – chemical killers. After all, who would want to eat what you just sprayed all over the plants? Most of the time a thorough shower will get rid of the pests. You may also want to consider a short period of quarantine underneath a see-through plastic bag.

Wort	Site	Sow out or buy in pot	Notes
basil Ocimum basilicum	sunny; warm, protected from wind partial shade	sow out; do not cover with soil	there are some special varieties for the balcony with small leaves and bushy growth; basil Marseille yields well, good pot plant; variegated varieties such as "dark opal" are pretty
chervil Anthriscus cerefolium	sunny to partial shade	sow out; do not cover with soil	re-sow every two to three weeks; chervil, regardless of a smooth or serrated leaved variety, makes for a beautiful contrast to flowering plants in a plant box
chives Allium schoenoprassum	full sun to decently lit conditions; warm	pot plant	never ever let the soil dry out between watering; harvest carefully so that the plant can grow back
coriander Coriandrum sativum	sunny; warm, protected from wind	sow out; cover with soil	to ensure a continued supply of fresh coriander re-sow approximately every 8 weeks
dill Anethum graveolens	sunny; warm	sow out	not all varieties are suitable for growing in the pot; ask at your local garden centre for dwarf varieties, one of which is called "delicate" (but names may vary); re-sow every two to three weeks
lavender Lavandula angustifolia	sunny to partial shade	pot plant	dwarf varieties such as the 'Canary' lavender (Lavandula minutolii) or the southern Spanish lavender (Lavandula lanata) are ideal for either the flower box or the windowsill
lemon balm Melissa officinalis	sunny and very warm	pot plant	keep the soil slightly moist; take care not to choose a pot too small as the plant likes to have plenty of space; lemon balm comes in quite a number of attractive variegated varieties
lemon grass Cymbopogon citratus	full sun; warm	pot plant	requires sufficient water supply, fertilise every now and then; essential to move indoors during the cold winter months
oregano Origanum vulgare	sunny to partial shade	sow out; do not cover with soil; slow germination	especially the small and bushy variety of "compactum" is ideally suited for growing in pots; even the strong Greek oregano (O. vulgare subsp. hirtum) is available as a dwarf variety
parsley Petroselinum crispum	sunny to partial shade	sow out; also as a pot plant	parsley may be easy to sow out but since it is a frequently used favourite in the kitchen, it may be worth to splash out and get a decent pot plant
peppermint Mentha x piperita	full sun; warm, protected	pot plant	peppermint loves it a little moist so take care not to let the soil dry out, avoid stagnant water though; pineapple mint (Mentha suaveolens 'Variegata') makes for an ideal pot plant
rosemary Rosmarinus officinalis	full sun	sow out; also as a pot plant	the varieties "blue winter" and "arp" are supposed to withstand freezing temperatures – even when kept in a pot; the variety "Miss Jessops" with a height of 50 cm/1 ½ feet is ideal for the windowsill
sage Salvia officinalis	sunny to partial shade; warm	pot plant	variegated varieties such as the yellow-greenish "icterina" or the purple and green "purpurascens" are particularly attractive, while the small and compact "nana" variety makes for an ideal pot plant
tarragon Artemisia dracunculus	full sun; warm	sow out; also as a pot plant	German and French tarragon can only be propagated through either division or cuttings (buy pot plants); Russian tarragon, however, can be sown out
thyme Thymus vulgaris	sunny to partial shade	pot plant	the citric aromatic lemon thyme (T. x citriodorus) not only makes for an ideal seasoning but is also a very attractive specimen, especially as it exists with either white or colourful yellowish leaves
watercress Lepidium sativum	sunny; warm, protected	sow out; do not cover with soil	do not wait longer than 2 weeks until you re-sow; keep nice and moist; undemanding and reliable vitamin production throughout the winter months; will even germinate on moist kitchen towels
winter savory Satureja montana	sunny; warm, protected from wind partial shade	sow out; do not cover with soil	the bushy "pikanta" makes for an ideal pot plant; the lemony winter savory has a delightful aroma of lemons and is a true delicacy

Growing Herbs

Herbs, compared to other plants, are relatively undemanding and easy to care for – this does not mean, however, that you can just forget about them. They will only reach their full potential and thrive as they ought to if you give them exactly what they need. It is therefore not enough to simply put them anywhere in your garden where there might be a free space. Just like other plants they want the right conditions and only then will they reward you!

Placement and Lighting Conditions

As we have mentioned already, many herbs originate from around the Mediterranean region, i.e. they want and need a fair amount of warmth and, not to forget, sunlight. The sun is very important as the plants use the energy from the sun to produce their unique aromas. Consequently, the more heat and sunlight you can provide them with, the more they will repay you with their precious aroma. This does not mean, however, that the plants will want to be exposed to the baking sun all day long but a good five hours of sun is just the ticket. This can only be guaranteed on south, south west or even west facing patches. The best possible scenario would involve a slight slope as this would afford small and large plants an equal amount of light.

It is therefore a good idea to give those plants that come from the Mediterranean the sunniest site available. The ideal place would be protected from the wind in front of a light wall which can reflect the sun and stores the sun's energy and heat. Another possibility would be in front of dense hedges or fully overgrown fences. If you do not have any walls that afford protection, you will have to use what mother nature provides, i.e. tall plants such as sunflowers or sweet corn. This need not involve a total upheaval of your beds – herbs will require protection and cover only from the side where the weather comes from.

Our native herbs are quite different. They will thrive even in semi-shady positions. However, they still need light and especially air. Even though common sorrel, lovage, borage or peppermint may be used to more moisture, they will not tolerate a site that is too wet and shady.

The Right Soil

Herbs are not fussy when it comes to soil. They will be quite happy with just about any permeable humus you put them in. Some of the most common and therefore important varieties such as rosemary, sage or thyme even prefer meagre, chalky, sandy to stony ground which is not surprising because that reflects the conditions from where they come from. If the soil is dry and poor, so much the better. Even though most undemanding herbs will survive in almost all kinds of soil, it is a good idea to prepare the ground properly before planting to guarantee the best possible conditions. An alternative would be to choose those plants that are comfortable with what you have.

To get a rough idea of what sort of soil you have in your garden, you can try the "mud-test": transfer a little soil from your garden into a glass and top up with water. Give everything a good stir and leave to rest for a while. You will notice how the individual components will separate and become visible. Sand, for example, will sink to the bottom while humus floats on the top and clay will make the contents of your glass murky.

This simple test, the "mud-test", enables you to find out more about the type of soil you are dealing with. To give you an idea here are some pure samples. Left: garden soil rich in humus, centre: sandy soil, right: clay.

A good idea apart from the mud-test is to check the pH value of your soil. It should lie somewhere between 6 and 7. These pH-kits are readily available from your local garden centre.

- Sandy soil is extremely permeable and consequently very dry and rather poor in nutrients. Some mature compost and perhaps a little clay, however, will lend these soils structure and richness. You may want to add extra nutrients in the form of bonemeal. This way even sandy soils will be quite capable of retaining at least some moisture.
- Loamy and clayey soils tend to get compacted. This makes it very difficult for water to drain off and the risk of waterlogging is very high. There is nothing for it, you will have to dig and dig deep, mixing in sand and mature compost. The sharp grains of sand will literally cut through the compacted soil and the humus will provide it with the necessary nutrients.
- Dark humus – the professional also refers to it as sandy loam – is ideal for most plants and all it needs is a little mature compost every now and then.

Water Supply

The same rule that applies to all other living creatures also goes for herbs: they simply cannot survive without water. While many herbs are able to withstand some periods of drought because they stem from a generally arid environment, the individual water supply has to be spot on.

How often you have to water them depends on a number of different factors, the most important being of course both weather and soil. A sandy, permeable soil will not be able to store enough moisture to satisfy your plants' desire and you will have to resort to watering your garden come the warm summer months. Peaty soils are not too different in that their water retaining qualities are poor. This is the kind of soil which your local garden centre sells for plant boxes. Once a peaty soil has dried out, it is very difficult to get it to retain water again. The only solution here is a total immersion in water.

The ideal soil to have with regard to water supply is one rich in humus. These soils are capable of retaining enough moisture to satisfy our herbs even during prolonged warm spells. If you do have to resort to watering you should only do so in the early morning. The plants will then have enough time to absorb the water before it evaporates. And just in case the leaves got splattered with drops of water, they can dry off quickly enough so as not to give those moisture loving snails or diseases a chance to attack your plant.

By the way, the best water for your plants comes straight out of a rain barrel. It has the right temperature and oxygen levels for your plants. Water from the tap will do as well, of course. But be careful: it should not be too cold as this could cause severe shock to your plants.

Nutrient Supply

It is usually not necessary to apply extra fertiliser and should only be considered if there is no other possible solution to your problem. Herbs prefer light fare as far as nutrients go and will react allergically to any attempts of fertilisation – regardless of whether you want to do them a favour or not. Too many nutrients will cause them to produce too much greenery and not enough aroma. Another unwanted side-effect is that they will become more susceptible to diseases and pests. A good soil rich in humus will be totally sufficient for your plants and all you have to do is add a little mature compost in the spring and carefully rake it into the top layer of your soil. Herbs with a very strong aroma should never be fertilised.

If you must fertilise, make sure to use only organic material such as bonemeal or other organic compounds. Better and milder are liquid manures. They are also easy to make yourself. All you have to do is fill a plastic barrel or a large bucket with nettles or horsetail. You can also add some garden waste such as leftover herbs. Top everything up with water, give it a good stir and leave for 14 days. Do not cover. Unfortunately it will start smelling a little, but this is nature's way of telling you that your liquid manure is ready. Add to your watering can (1:10) and apply once in the spring and once in the autumn – no more for the sake of your plants.

One thing you should avoid at all costs is synthetically produced liquid fertilisers. The plants absorb the nutrients extremely quickly and will therefore concentrate on producing leaves and leaves only. The aroma will almost disappear completely.

You can make excellent liquid manure using horsetail (left), stinging nettles (centre) or common comfrey (right) – both ecologically sound and of course absolutely free.

Regular Trimming is a Must

The best thing you can possibly afford your herbs is regular trimming or, even better, frequent harvesting. A steady harvest of fresh shoots is not only an ideal way of preventing the plants from becoming woody but will also promote further growth. The herbs will also retain a compact shape, will not become leggy and will delight you with their wonderful aromas on a continuous basis. Do not be afraid! All herbs grown for their fresh leaves can be trimmed once or twice during the growing season without any harm being done. On the contrary, they will thank you for it with a wealth of fresh young leaves. As an example, you really should cut back both peppermint and lemon balm during flowering and again in the late summer. Woody perennials such as lavender, sage, rue or thyme are quite happy if you trim them once in spring and cut them back again after they have flowered or before the winter respectively.

TOP TIP

Lavender, rosemary and sage will benefit from cutting back. Trim them by a third in the autumn.

Some herbs really do benefit from being cut back before the winter. Often it is the only possibility of getting awkward looking plants into shape. Take care, though, not to cut back too much. Always leave enough old growth, approximately a hand's breadth above ground, otherwise the plant will suffer. The herb's own rotting leaves and dead branches will provide a kind of mulch which protects the delicate buds until the spring comes. Wait until spring to cut back woody herbs.

Do yourself and your plants a big favour: take great care when buying tools for your garden. Good quality and workmanship are a must. Always go for two edged shears and secateurs because single edge cutting tools often damage plants by crushing the stalk or bark during the process of cutting. Your shears should not be too big either; comfortable handling is important. The same is true of secateurs. You have to be at ease holding them and the security mechanism should be easy to operate. If you have to cut through wood and branches, a sturdy tree pruner will do the job but the average gardener should start with shears and secateurs. These tools will certainly be sufficient for your herb garden. Take care of your tools and keep them clean from bits of earth or plant. Not only will it prolong their life, but it will also prevent the spreading of diseases. Also make sure they are nice and sharp because only a sharp edge will cut properly and not damage your plant.

Preparing for Winter

How well your aromatic and medicinal herbs will cope with the cold season depends on the particular variety as well as plant origin and age. If in doubt or if you live in an exposed part of the country, it is just as good to protect them with a layer of dry leaves, some evergreen coniferous branches or even bark mulch. This measure will create an insulating cushion of air and prevent the roots from being exposed to the severe cold. During icy cold weather interrupted by warm spells, the cushion will also stop the roots from the destructive freeze and thaw cycles. Should a cold spell catch you by surprise and the roots of your plants should freeze, there really is very little you can do to save them.

The denser the layer you covered your plants with the more important is the timely removal and loosening of the earth around it in the spring. It should not be done later than when the first signs of life such as shoots appear through the protective layer. But do not dispose of it completely, as ground frost can be very unpredictable. Those herbs that cannot survive out in the open – this will be most of the Mediterranean plants – have to be removed from the ground and transferred to pots so you can easily move them inside. Rosemary or laurel are two prime candidates for such a move.

Provide your winter guests with a bright and cool site that is absolutely frost free. This could be a bright cellar, the stairway or even a rarely heated bedroom. The ideal solution would obviously be a conservatory with special heating. As the plants use this period to rest and recuperate you can reduce watering to a bare minimum. Take care, however, not to let them dry out completely as this would damage them. Check every now and then. Before you know it, you will have developed a feel for the necessary amount of moisture. If you go through the bother of covering your herb bed with perforated foil, in early spring it will repay your time and faith by providing you with fresh greenery two to three weeks earlier than if you just left it to itself.

This lavender plant is surrounded by evergreen coniferous branches and will survive the winter.

Herbs – Healthy and Strong

Generally speaking, herbs are remarkably hardy and robust and fall seldom victim to diseases or pests such as aphids, flea beetles, nematodes (like root-knot nematodes) or white flies. Prerequisites for a healthy herb garden, bed or herbaceous border are: the right site and aspect with regard to soil, sunshine, warmth and fresh air. It is also important to know which plants should be adjacent to each other and which ones to avoid as neighbours. The right combination of plants can ward off many a disease or pest.

The name of the game is mixed cultivation. This is a method that has been tried and tested in the field of organic vegetable cultivation because it exploits the different combinations of plants to promote growth and prevent disease and pests to which normal monoculture is so prone. Intensely aromatic herbs, for example, are an invaluable tool to ward off pests – the most famous case of a successful symbiosis is probably the combination of roses and lavender to protect against aphids. Other herbs and worts even increase the taste of certain vegetables: everybody knows about summer savory and runner beans for one and dill and cucumbers to name but two possibilities.

Naturally, while there are some combinations that go well together – please refer to the table "Good Neighbours" on page 53 – there are others that spell disaster. It would not be surprising if more than one amateur gardener was on the verge of a nervous breakdown because his or her

Herb	Good Neighbours	Effect
basil Ocimum basilicum	tomatoes, cucumber, courgette	drives away cabbage white moth and white fly; prevents mildew; has antibacterial properties; attracts bees, good for pollination
borage Borago officinalis	dill, marjoram, oregano, cucumber, cabbage	attracts insects, great for bees; generally wards off pests; good roots that loosen the soil
chamomile Matricaria chamomilla	parsley, onions, vegetables	protects against nematodes and thrips; prevents grey mould, mildew, mites; wards off white cabbage moth and mice; encourages both growth and general health
chervil Anthriscus cerefolium	lettuce, kohlrabi, onions	aromatic substances protect against ants and aphids; repels snails; improves general health of neighbouring plants; increases their aroma
dill Anethum graveolens	borage, chives, onions, cucumber, cabbage, carrots, red beetroot	increases resistance to pests and diseases of neighbouring plants, improves germination of neighbouring seeds; aromatic essences ward off root pests; attracts bees
garlic Allium sativum	berries, cucumber, carrots, fruit trees, lettuce, tomatoes, roses	has preventative qualities against fungal infections and mites; antibacterial; gets rid of mice (but not voles)
lavender Lavandula angustifolia	roses	antibacterial properties in case of fungal infections; repels ants and to a certain degree aphids
marigold Calendula	potatoes, cabbage, tomatoes	antibacterial and antiviral; effective against nematodes, wireworms; increases yield and improves overall soil quality
nasturtium Tropaeolum majus	broccoli, cabbage, fruit trees	attracts aphids and woolly aphids as well as white cabbage moth thus keeping them off neighbouring plants; repels ants, caterpillars and snails; has preventative qualities against fungal infections
onion Allium cepa	dill, marjoram, oregano, parsley, rosemary, thyme, strawberries, carrots	protects against fungal infections and spider mites, some repellent properties against nematodes and carrot fly
peppermint Mentha x piperita	cabbage, fruit trees, vines	good against mildew; repels white cabbage moth, ants, flea beetles, potato beetles, mice; improves aroma of neighbouring plants
rosemary Rosmarinus officinalis	chives, sage, onions, cabbage, carrots	acts as a disinfectant; aromatic substances protect against white cabbage moth and carrot fly; also effective against ants, aphids, caterpillars and snails
sage Salvia officinalis	beans, peas, fennel, rosemary, lettuce, vines, hyssop	has antibacterial and antiseptic properties; preventative against fungal infections; repels white cabbage moth, aphids, caterpillars, snails, carrot flies; increases aroma of both fennel and lettuce
stinging nettle Urtica diocia	peppermint, cucumber, cabbage, tomatoes, carrots, lettuce, kohlrabi, strawberries, raspberries	good against aphids, spider mites, white flies; beneficial to general health; improves taste of neighbouring plants
summer savory Satureja hortensis	beans, onions	wards off black bean aphids; aromatic agents increase yield and improve the taste of beans, encourages growth of onions
thyme Thymus vulgaris	general protective properties	has antiseptic and antiviral properties; suppresses couch grass; attracts bees, bumblebees and butterflies; lemon thyme repels both blackfly and ants
wormwood Artemisia absinthium	black currants, leeks	protects black currants against rust; repels ants, leek moths, aphids, mites, snails; wormwood liquid manure, if applied regularly, keeps the garden free of pests

beautiful combination would not grow. The reason might well have been essential oils or root excretions or even substances produced by leaves that rain distributes in the soil and hinders the other plant from growing properly. However, it may not only be the neighbouring plant that can stunt growth, but also the site or the lack of movement. For example, parsley cannot stand its own smell and has to be moved every year (please also refer to pages 52 and 53). You should mix all your annuals as much as possible, sowing them out in a slightly different place every year. Not only do the plants like it but it also prevents the soil from being robbed of a particular nutrient.

Medicine for Herbs Straight from the Garden

Your plants will not suffer from pests and diseases very often. However, when they do, nature has the right answer for all eventualities. Most of the time, however, mechanical measures will be quite sufficient. In practice this means cutting back infected branches in case of rust or mildew, collecting caterpillars or the setting up of snail or vole traps. Chemical means are a definite no-no if any those plants you might want to spray end up on your plate. It definitely is not healthy and should be taboo!

Tansy prevents fungal infections and repels insects.

Herbal essences, on the other hand, are totally unobjectionable. Liquids of all kinds are easily and quickly made. As a rule use somewhere between 200 g/7 oz and 1 kg/2 lbs of fresh plant material for every 10 l of water, taking care that the mixture does not start fermenting. Below are some examples with the amount of plant material needed in brackets:

- stinging nettle tea (200 g/7 oz): spray undiluted against aphids;
- garlic tea (75 g/2 ½ oz): spray undiluted against aphids, spider mites, preventative properties against fungal infections;
- tansy tea (300 g/11 oz): spray undiluted against mites and other insects, preventative properties against fungal infections; can be mixed with horsetail tea;
- horsetail tea (300 g/11 oz): dilute 1:5 and spray on fungal infections;
- wormwood tea (300 g/11 oz): spray undiluted against flea beetles, aphids, caterpillars and ants.

Wormwood tea is a reliable way to combating flea beetles, aphids, caterpillars and ants.

Sowing Out, Planting and Propagation

Whether you prefer sowing out your own seeds or producing new plants by means of layering or offsets, whether you take cuttings, divide the root stock or buy pot plants from your local garden centre is entirely up to you and the amount of time you have on your hands. Naturally, you will have to take into account the plants themselves.

This is where herbs can prove to be quite fussy. For example, although some worts can be grown from seed, it is a very tedious process since they produce very few seeds. French tarragon (Artemisia dracunculus var. sativa), but not its cousin the Russian tarragon, is an example of a plant displaying this kind of behaviour. Peppermint (Mentha x piperita) is another specimen just as many of the variegated and over-bred varieties of both thyme and sage hybrids. Either they are sterile or their seeds do not produce the same plants as is the case for F1-hybrids. But even these specimen can be propagated relatively easily. You can either take cuttings or divide the root stock.

Wort	Culture	Site/Soil	Sowing Out	Notes
anise Pimpinella anisum	annual	sunny, warm; permeable soil	from April onwards	cover with soil
basil Ocimum basilicum	annual	sunny, bright and warm, protected from wind; light, moist soil	from middle/end of May	do not cover with soil; cannot stand ground frost, requires high germination temperature
borage Borago officinalis	annual	sunny to partial shade, likes rich, chalky soil	from April–June	cover seeds with soil; self sower
burnet saxifrage Sanguisorba minor	perennial	sunny to partial shade; dry, light soil	from March/April onwards	difficult to move because of long tap roots
caraway Carvum carvi	biannual	full sun; nice and moist clayey soil	from April/May onwards	do not cover seeds with soil
chervil Anthriscus cerefolium	annual	partial shade; reasonably moist soil	March to September	do not cover seeds with soil, self sower
chives Allium schoenoprassum	oniony, perennial	sunny to partial shade; chalky soil rich in nutrients	sow out from March/April onwards; divide every 2 to 3 years in spring or autumn	optional removal of flowers to promote growth of leaves
coriander Coriandrum sativum	annual	full sun, warm; light slightly alkaline soil	April	cover seeds with soil; does not like fennel
curry plant Helichrysum italicum ssp. serotinum	perennial	full sun; permeable and poor soil	from May onwards	requires protection from the cold
dill Anethum graveolens	annual	full sun, protected from wind, soil rich in humus	from March/April to June at the latest	change site annually; does not like fennel
fennel Foeniculum vulgare var. dulce	biannual, perennial	full sun, warm, protected; chalky soil rich in nutrients	March/April	cover seeds with a little soil, does not like dill nor coriander
garden sorrel Rumex acetosa	perennial	sunny to partial shade; moist soil rich in humus	sow out in spring; division possible in spring or autumn	change site every five years
garlic Allium sativum	annual, biannual	sunny; light soil rich in humus	plant out bulbs March–April and July–August	possible to sow out in spring
hyssop Hyssopus officinalis	perennial	full sun and warm; permeable, chalky soil	sow out from April; rooted cuttings in spring; division in spring	cut back to 20 cm/8 inches above ground in spring
lavender Lavandula angustifolia	perennial	sunny; dry, permeable, chalky soil	sow out from April onwards, cuttings from early summer	cut back by a third in spring
lemon balm Melissa officinale	perennial	sunny to partial shade, warm and protected; permeable soil rich in humus	sow out from April, cuttings from spring onwards, division in spring	cut back properly in spring/autumn
lovage Levisticum officinalis	perennial	sunny to partial shade; moist, rich soil	sow out or divide April, May or autumn	careful not to harm the main shoot when dividing the plant
marigold Calendula officinalis	annual	full sun to protected but bright; fresh to medium soil, no waterlogging	from May onwards	keeps on flowering if deadheaded regularly

Wort	Culture	Site/Soil	Sowing Out	Notes
marjoram Origanum majorana	annual	full sun, warm; light, permeable soil	from May onwards	do not cover seeds with soil; ideal for windowsill
mugwort Artemisia vulgaris	perennial	sunny; dry, sandy and poor soil	from middle of May onwards	do not cover seeds with soil; heavy spread so only plant out one specimen
mustard Brassica juncea	annual	sunny to partial shade; undemanding	March to September	self sower; during the winter quite happy indoors
nasturtium Tropaeolum majus	annual	sunny to partial shade; delicate plant; soil rich in humus and nutrients	April/May	sow directly in plant boxes/pots, place outside from May onwards
oregano Origanum vulgare	perennial	full sun and warm; try, chalky soil	sow out March/April; propagation through cuttings or division in early summer	do not cover seeds with soil, slow germinator
parsley Petroselinum crispum	biannual	sunny to partial shade; soil rich in humus and nutrients	from March onwards	takes 4 weeks to germinate; change site every year
peppermint Mentha x piperita	biannual	sunny to partial shade; light, moist soil, can be alkaline	sow out from April/June; division or layering in spring	plant layered branches virtually horizontally
ramson Allium ursinum	oniony, perennial	partial shade; good soil rich in humus and nutrients	sowing out August to February, bulbs in the autumn and March/April	requires stratification
rosemary Rosmarinus officinalis	perennial	full sun, warm, protected; permeable sandy soil or rich in humus	sow or plant out from April/May; rooted cuttings from August	raising from seeds takes time, easier to buy seedlings/take cuttings
sage Salvia officinalis	perennial	full sun; permeable, reasonably dry poor soil	sow out and cuttings from end of April	do not cover seeds with soil; cut back in spring if necessary
summer savory Satureja hortensis	mostly perennial	sunny, undemanding, prefers dry, chalky soil	April/May-July	do not cover seeds with soil
tarragon Artemisia dracunculus	perennial	sunny to partial shade, warm, protected; moist soil rich in humus	French tarragon requires division; sow out Russian tarragon from April onwards	cut back in the autumn
thyme Thymus vulgaris	perennial	full sun and warm; reasonably dry, sandy soil	sowing out, separation and offsets from April/May onwards	do not cover seeds with soil; raising seeds takes patience, easier to buy seedlings
valerian Valeriana officinalis	perennial	sunny; soil rich in humus and nutrients, can be clay	March/April or September/October; plant separation in spring or autumn	do not cover seeds with soil; must thin seedlings
watercress Lepidium sativum	annual, biannual	sunny to partial shade; fresh to moist soil	from March onwards	do not cover seeds with soil, self sower
winter savory Satureja montana	perennial	sunny, protected, prefers poor soil	sow out or divide plant from April onwards or in the autumn	do not cover seeds with soil; woody after 2nd year
woodruff Galium odoratum	perennial	shady; light, moist soil	division in spring, rich soil; sow out late summer/autumn	requires stratification
wormwood Artemisia absinthium	perennial	sunny; permeable, rather dry soil, undemanding	rooted cuttings or division in spring	do not place next to medicinal plants as it curbs growth

Raising from Seed

In nature plants continually propagate themselves from seeds – the same goes for your herbs. Some are so efficient at this that you cannot but be amazed at how that marigold, borage, caraway or dandelion managed to get there. After all, you never planted it nor intended it to be exactly there! The plants that have grown from self sowing are usually more robust than those raised from packet seeds. It might therefore be a good idea to move those plants you find "out in the open" to your herb bed rather than raising a weaker plant from seeds.

Normally, however, it is up to the amateur gardener to do a bit of Do-It-Yourself. Annuals and biannuals such as basil, dill, watercress, borage, chervil, marigold and parsley are ideally suited to raising from seed bought at the local garden centre. There are a number of different ways of sowing. You can do it on the windowsill indoors, in a greenhouse or conservatory, in a hotbed or out in the open. If you choose the first method, you will have reasonably big plants in good time for planting out. But do not start earlier than March unless, of course, you have special lamps that provide the seedlings with the much needed sunlight.

Certain requirements have to be satisfied for the seeds to germinate: they demand sufficient amounts of moisture, warmth, air and light. Most seeds germinate when temperatures start climbing steadily and the days are getting longer again. But no rule without exceptions: there are special cases such as rue, ramson or woodruff that require what the professional calls stratification, i.e. they need the cold to be tempted in the first place. Seeds from these plants have to be sown out where you want them to grow no sooner than autumn.

If you want to start early, however, you should either use small pots or shallow trays filled with special seedling compost (fertiliser free), leaving a 1 cm/½ inch gap to the top of the tray. Water the compost and sow the seeds thinly and evenly. Cover the seeds with a soil

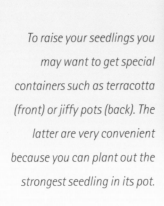

To raise your seedlings you may want to get special containers such as terracotta (front) or jiffy pots (back). The latter are very convenient because you can plant out the strongest seedling in its pot.

or not as the case may be. As a rule of thumb, the layer of soil should be about two or three times the diameter of the seed. Press everything down gently and spray with water. Transfer the tray to a bright, warm spot and wait. It might be a good idea to cover the tray with a see-through lid to reduce evaporation. It may take some time until you see the first bit of green appear.

Only the Strongest Make it All the Way

Once the seed has germinated and become a seedling, i.e. the first bits of proper greenery have appeared rather than the seed leaves, it is time to transfer it to a pot with soil rich in humus. This is also the ideal time for thinning (see right). If you have raised it in a jiffy pot, the approach is slightly different: select the strongest seedling and cut down all the others. This will give the strongest one enough space until you can move it to its final destination in your garden. The advantage of this method: the tiny roots remain intact – during thinning you will invariably damage them – and the plant can continue to grow as though nothing has happened. Whatever the method you opt for, your young plants will repay you for a nice bright, warm site with a little sunshine.

Depending on the prevailing weather you may want to get your plants used to the outside world bit by bit. To do so, place the pots in your garden or on the balcony. Alternatively, open up the hotbeds. Come nighttime you should take them inside again or close the hotbeds respectively. After 3 to 4 weeks of hardening your herbs, they will be quite capable of surviving out in the open. Remember that the final move is very stressful for the plant – do it only during good weather.

TOP TIP *A dibber or some such implement is a very useful tool for levering the seedling or young plant ever so gently from its surroundings.*

Cutting out the Middleman – Sowing Out Directly

From the middle of May onwards, prevailing weather conditions are stable enough to risk sowing out your seeds directly in the open. Those who still want to make sure that nothing goes wrong can set up their own little nursery in a sheltered spot in the garden. This is not such a bad idea because in the event of a cold spell, it is easier to cover the spot with a protective foil or some other means of keeping the seedlings warm. Take a few seeds into the palm of your hand – not too many – and spread them evenly over a large area. Again, only the strongest will reach their final destination. Useful are seedlings embedded into special tape available from your local garden centre. All you have to do is make a small groove, insert the tape, water properly and cover if appropriate.

Cuttings

Woody herbs such as lavender, rosemary, sage, hyssop, winter savory, oregano and thyme can be propagated through cuttings anytime between June and August. To do so cut off the first 5 to 10 cm/2 to 4 inches of vigorous, healthy fresh shoots. Take care to use a very sharp knife so as to stress the plant as little as possible. Even secateurs would damage the cutting too severely. Remove all lower leaves and transfer the cutting into a glass  filled with water and wait for it to develop roots. Many herb cuttings, however, can also be planted in special moist cutting compost.

Now move your cuttings to a reasonably shady place in the garden or the windowsill. A sufficient water supply at this stage is vital. The telltale signs that everything worked out fine and the plant has developed roots are the appearance of leaves. You can move the plant out into the garden and to its final destination as soon as the young plant is strong enough. This is a wonderfully easy and very cheap method of creating young plants which, if the whole process was started early enough, can be planted out the same year they were raised.

A rooting lavender cutting

Root Cuttings

A similar method of propagation is that of taking root cuttings. This method works for example for peppermint, meadowsweet or dandelions. Uncover the roots, remove any surplus organic material and divide the main rhizome into 4 to 8 cm/1 ½ to 3 ½ inch long pieces. The top should be cut straight, the bottom at an angle. Insert the cuttings into a pot filled with special cutting compost. Cover with a spattering of earth, approximately a finger thick and transfer outside to the hotbed or onto the windowsill. Again, watering is the key. The soil must not dry out nor should it be too moist. Repot the seedlings once you can see new growth appearing. Continue in the fashion described above until they are hardy enough to be planted out.

Layering and Offsets

Some hardy herbs can be propagated by means of layering long shoots that remain close to the ground. Peppermint (Mentha x piperita), for example, does not need any encouragement and does so by itself. It develops these creeping shoots which start rooting as soon as they establish contact with the soil. This strategy is so successful that peppermint, if left unchecked, will quite happily take over half your garden. A good idea is to grow it in a large pot without the bottom to act as a barrier for the roots. Still, you may want to keep an eye on it.

In the case of other, less virile plants you have to lend a hand. Select a long shoot and bend it until it touches the ground, taking care not to break it. Make a number of incisions – not too deep, you do not want to cut through the shoot – and fasten it to the ground with a bit of wire or other suitable material before covering it with a little compost mixed with sand. Some plants respond quicker than others to this treatment and roots develop in the same year. Others may take up to three years. Following successful root formation – remove from soil carefully to have a look – you can cut the shoot off its mother plant and transfer to its final destination. This propagation method is preferred for sage, lemon balm and hyssop.

Peppermint "clones" from the
mother plant's subterranean
shoots

Division

By far the simplest way of plant propagation is division. This method is especially suited to perennial bushes such as lemon balm, tarragon, valerian or chives but annual parsley will also reward you with new plants. The best time for division is a resting period, either during spring or the autumn. Depending on how strong a plant is, you can either divide it with a sharp spade or, alternatively, you can dig up the whole plant and cut it into two using a sharp knife. Some plants are even hardy enough to withstand the rather crude method of pulling the roots apart.

Once the two specimen are separated simply plant each one into its already prepared spot – always the same depth as the "cloned" mother plant. Water well.

Roots that have had plenty of space to spread are
easily separated following a cut with a sharp knife.

Place the separated plants into the already prepared spot.
Water well.

Herb Harvest

Growing plants is an exciting pastime in itself, but harvesting the fruits of your labour is a different matter entirely! The same goes for eating and keeping those delightful aromas! If you want to use the herbs immediately, simply cut off what you need throughout the growing season – as long as their shoots and leaves are still green and aromatic. Although many evergreen herbs will supply you with their goods throughout the winter, do not harvest during frost. Sage, thyme and rosemary, for example, do not mind being plucked in the winter to help ward off colds and sore throats.

When to Harvest

Each and every wort reaches a peak in the year when it grows the best produce. This is the time that the concentration of aromatic ingredients or constituents is at its highest. For normal everyday use in the kitchen this fact may not be all that important, but it is of interest to those who may want to conserve or keep the fruits of their seasonings or medicinal plants. With many herbs this peak more or less coincides with the flowering period. After that, the plant requires all its strength to form the flowers followed by seeds. This strenuous task does not go unnoticed when it comes to aroma. The best time of year to harvest each herb is listed in the tables on pages 64 and 65 and the table of descriptions on pages 125 and 126. Please bear in mind, though, that these should be seen more as indications because the exact time is largely dependant on region and weather conditions and can change from year to year. The best thing is to know your plants well because this enables you to catch them at their peak. Always harvest on a sunny morning after the dew has evaporated but all essential oils are still present and have not fallen prey to the midday sun.

To Cut or to Pull?

Weather you prefer cutting off individual leaves or simply rip them off by hand is more a question of philosophy than anything else. There is no hard and fast rule – it is entirely up to you. It obviously makes sense to have a good pair of secateurs or a sharp knife around for woody varieties such as thyme, sage or rosemary. Bear in mind that the implement should not only be sharp, but also clean so as not to endanger the mother plant. A fungal infection is the last thing you want.

For those with sensitive skin or allergic reactions, it may be a good idea to wear gardening gloves. Special care should also be taken when harvesting St. John's wort, rue or wormwood.

The best containers for gathering herbs are airy baskets, but a shoe carton with a number of holes will do just as well. You should avoid shopping or freezer bags made from plastic as any evaporated liquid cannot escape and remains trapped inside – the plants sweat and the resulting heat will cause them to wilt before you know it.

How Much and What?

Do not just harvest whatever is the "nearest" and do not raid plants! Those who are after larger amounts for keeping easily run danger of harvesting more than the plant can cope with. However, if you have plenty of specimen so that you can spare enough plants for "immediate" use until the end of the season, you are free to cut perennials back by half. Annuals can even take a little more punishment and you can trim them up to two thirds back.

Take care not to harvest more than you can actually use right there and then. Essential oils have a habit of evaporating very quickly.

It goes without saying that you only use the very best your plant has to offer for long term keeping. Some herbs are harvested more or less completely – this includes just about everything that sticks more than a hand's width out of the ground. It sounds severe, but you should do it just as the

TOP TIP

Shake your herbs thoroughly following the harvest to loosen pieces of dirt and shake off insects. Remove discoloured or injured leaves.

plant starts flowering. Individual leaves and stalks are usually harvested when young so they do not have a chance to get too chewy. Harvest large leaves individually. For some plants, it is true that you harvest their flowers or buds, usually straight after they have opened. Large flowers should be removed with or without the supporting stalk – it can always be disposed of later. Apart from the tasty leaves, seeds is what you are after when you think of caraway, fennel or dill. These are harvested when they are mature, but not so mature that the plant starts to shed them all by itself. Other edible parts of plants include the root stock (rhizome), bulbs or onions. In the latter case, you harvest during the growing season once those parts of the plant above ground have died off. You will find further information on what to harvest from which plant in the tables on pages 64 and 65.

Wort	What to Harvest	When to Harvest	Notes
anise Pimpinella anisum	leaves, seeds	June to September	flowers or ground seeds excellent for fruit salads or aromatic potpourris
basil Ocimum basilicum	leaves, flowers	June to August; all year round if pot plant	to dry the leaves harvest just before flowering; otherwise, from bottom to top
borage Borago officinalis	leaves, flowers	from May onwards	flowers serve as attractive decorations for jellies, drinks, soups or even the table
burnet saxifrage Sanguisorba minor	leaves, tops of shoots	May to November	one of the first sources of vitamin C in spring, famous ingredient of the German "green sauce"
caraway Carvum carvi	leaves, seeds	June to September	caraway is a self sower if in a good place
chervil Anthriscus cerefolium	shoots, leaves, flowers	May to November, harvest as soon as 6 weeks after sowing out	never gather from unknown sites, easy to confuse with the poisonous hemlock!
chives Allium schoenoprassum	leaves, flowers	April to November	to get good growth, cut off woody flower stems; remove flowers
coriander Coriandrum sativum	leaves, seeds	seeds in August; leaves at start of flowering period	the more often you sow, the longer the harvest period
curry plant Helichrysum italicum ssp. serotinum	leaves, flowers	all year round	flowers serve as attractive decorations for potpourris, leaves give soups a hint of curry
dill Anethum graveolens	leaves, shoots, seeds	leaves all year round, seeds on turning brown, flowers as they appear	if your dill is happy, it will sow out itself; packed with minerals, excellent accompaniment to a spring diet
fennel Foeniculum vulgare var. dulce	tops of shoots, seeds	seeds August to September, leaves all year round	you can also use the leaves of the related vegetable fennel as seasonings; seeds only mature in full sun
garden sorrel Rumex acetosa	leaves with stalks	from May to the flowering period	contains a lot of vitamin C, but also oxalic acid which is poisonous in high dosages
garlic Allium sativum	cloves	June to September	choose native varieties
hyssop Hyssopus officinalis	leaves, flowers, top of shoots	June to August	decorative blue flowers, aroma is reminiscent of frankincense
lavender Lavandula angustifolia	leaves, tops of shoots, flowers	July to August	classical neighbour for roses
lemon balm Melissa officinale	leaves, top of shoots	May to October, all year round	self sower; tends to spread and requires some sort of root barrier
lovage Levisticum officinalis	leaves, roots	May to October	very vigorous, requires some barrier for roots, will take over the bed otherwise
marigold Calendula officinalis	fully opened flowers	June to September	can be used instead of saffron; attractive decoration for teas, salads, potpourris

Wort	What to Harvest	When to Harvest	Notes
marjoram Origanum majorana	tops of shoots, flowers	from May/June onwards	marjoram can be cultivated as an annual or perennial plant, the latter is winter hardy; harvest from bottom to top
mugwort Artemisia vulgaris	leaves	right up to the flowering period	to dry remove whole stalks (prior to flowering period)
mustard Brassica juncea	young leaves, seeds	May to November	main ingredient of mustard made with its crushed seeds, vinegar, seasonings and sugar; leaves good in salads
nasturtium Tropaeolum majus	leaves, flowers, buds	May to October	buds can be used instead of capers; flowers serve as attractive decorations in salads
oregano Origanum vulgare	leaves, tops of shoots	April to October	harvest from bottom to top; if you want to dry harvest prior to flowering period
parsley Petroselinum crispum	leaves, stalks	May to December	parsley is relatively hardy, can therefore be harvested nearly all year round
peppermint Mentha x piperita	leaves, everything	June to October	pineapple mint or other special varieties are perfect for the kitchen
ramson Allium ursinum	leaves, flowers, bulb	right up to the flowering period	careful! easy to confuse with the poisonous leaves from the lilly of the valley. Crush leaves and check for typical garlic odour!
rosemary Rosmarinus officinalis	tops of shoots	May to September	ancient seasoning and medicinal plant; not really winter hardy
sage Salvia officinalis	leaves, flowers, tops of shoots	leaves all year round; just before flowering if dried	common sage is a perennial compared to some of its biannual cousins
summer savory Satureja hortensis	leaves, shoots	June to September	harvest shortly before and during the flowering period (for drying); cut back to a hand's width above ground
tarragon Artemisia dracunculus	tops of shoots, leaves	from May onwards, best late summer	French tarragon has a stronger taste than the Russian variety but is not hardy enough to survive the winter
thyme Thymus vulgaris	leaves, tops of shoots	May to September	tasty and interesting varieties include lemon and orange thyme
valerian Valeriana officinalis	roots	autumn of the second year	do not let it flower, if you want to use it for its medicinal qualities
watercress Lepidium sativum	leaves and tops of shoots before flowering period	once taller than 7 cm/ 3 inches, all year round	cut with scissors and use immediately; the undemanding plant will thrive on a windowsill even in winter
winter savory Satureja montana	leaves, top of shoots	all year round	perennial unlike its annual cousin summer savory; ideal for edgings
woodruff Galium odoratum	everything prior or during flowering period	May to June	leave to wilt for approximately 2 hours for aroma to develop
wormwood Artemisia absinthium	flowers, leaves	May to August	to dry cut off tops of shoots

Conserving Herbs

People have been brooding for a long time over how to keep the harvest of these valuable plants as fresh as possible for as long as possible. They have come up with a number of different ways of storing and conserving herbs including drying, preserving in vinegar or oil, alcohol, honey, sugar or salt. A more recent and very useful addition is the freezing of herbs.

Drying

The oldest and perhaps simplest method of conserving herbs is drying. As long as you do not have single leaves or flowers, tie the stalks together with a piece of thread and hang them out to dry. Make sure they are upside down. Take care that they get access to enough dry air to prevent rotting. A dry wall or washing line will do fine. Also important is that they are not exposed to full sunshine but much rather dry slowly in a shady but airy place. Furthermore, herbs that are to be dried should not be washed (!) as this could under certain circumstances promote fungal infection. A good shake should be sufficient to get rid of dust and insects. As attractive as these herb bunches may seem – both the kitchen and the bathroom are far too moist for your purposes. Storing them here is positively asking for trouble and it will not be long before a fungus or two will spoil your herbs.

A further possibility suitable for drying individual leaves or whole flowerheads are shallow boxes made of wood or fruit crates from your local greengrocer's. Place a piece of linen or muslin onto the wood and transfer the harvested herb in generous intervals. Turn "fleshy" parts of the plant every now and then to prevent them from rotting. Again, store in a shady but airy position to avoid spoilage.

Varieties known for their seeds include fennel, dill and caraway. Harvesting is not so simple as it sounds because once the seeds have reached maturity, a breath of fresh air is sufficient to spread them all over your bed. The solution is gathering individual seeds manually – if you find them, that is. It is a good idea to harvest relatively early when they are still moist from dew. Once again, tie into loose bunches and cover the seed pods with cotton bags or tissue paper. Leave plenty of room for the air to circulate. Now they are ready for hanging out to dry.

Unfortunately, not everybody has a suitable place for drying herbs at their disposal. In this case you may want to consider drying them over the oven. Open it a tad for the evaporated steam to escape and preheat to no more than 35 °C/95 °F – not a degree more or you will lose all essential oils. Place a few of the herbs on a sheet of aluminium foil and spread out well. A special drying apparatus available from your local garden centre is ideal for small quantities.

Your herbs are properly dried once the stalks become brittle, the leaves crumble and everything rustles nicely. It is best to keep only those parts with the highest concentration of essential oils, i.e. the leaves or flowers. It is now time to prepare them for easy storing. This is generally best done by rubbing the dried plant with your fingers. Break up the stalks. Once the whole plant is broken up into small pieces, transfer everything to air-tight containers – make sure that these are not too big because the extra air has a negative impact on the flavour. Screw-top jars or special tins will do nicely here. Do not forget to label everything carefully and note down the year of the harvest. This way you can be sure you know what you are dealing with and do not have to rely on your nose as to what kind of herb you have in front of you and whether it goes with what is in the pot.

Freezing

While drying is only really practicable for larger amounts, freezing is an ideal way of preserving smaller portions easily and quickly. Another benefit is that it preserves most of the active ingredients, especially vitamins. The drawback is that the aroma suffers from the shock of freezing. The best herbs for freezing are parsley, basil, summer savory, dill, tarragon, oregano or chives.

Remove damaged or spoiled leaves and thick stalks. You are free to freeze either the whole harvest or smaller portions in appropriately sized bags. If you freeze whole herbs you can always break them up at a later stage using a rolling pin while still in the freezer bag. Those herbs which are already chopped up can be frozen in small portions. Ideal for this are ice cubes into which you integrate the herbs. Use immediately on defrosting as the water from the ice cubes will make your herbs mushy and the longer you wait the less of the original aroma will survive.

On the following pages you will find basic recipes for other ways of conserving your seasonings. Feel free to experiment.

Herbal Vinegar

TOP TIP | *If you use herbs from your own herb patch, you probably do not need to wash them. However, if you rely on bought herbs from the supermarket or the greengrocer's, it is best to give them a good rinse and shake them dry.*

Basic recipe

4 tbs chopped herbs, fresh
or 3–4 fresh sprigs of any of the
following:
basil,
borage flowers,
tarragon,
dill,
laurel,
peppermint,
sage,
thyme,
lemon balm

Fruit or white wine vinegar

resealable glass bottle

Preservation in vinegar, oil or alcohol (please refer to pages 73 and 74) will keep your herbs for eons to come. This method relies on extracting the aroma from the herbs just for the acids of the vinegar, the oil or alcohol to absorb and thus preserve them:

To make 1 1/2 pints of herbal vinegar transfer approx. 4 tablespoons of chopped herbs or 3 to 4 sprigs into the bottle.

Top up with vinegar. Make sure that all the herbs are completely covered. Then give the bottle a little shake to release any air bubble that may have been trapped amongst the herbs.

Put the cork into the bottle or screw tight and leave to steep in a sunny place for approx. 2 to 3 weeks depending on the herbs used. Give a good shake every now and then. After this period, you can keep your herbal vinegar in darker places, too.

Herbal Oil

You really want to use very aromatic herbs to flavour oils such as basil, oregano, rosemary, sage, thyme or hyssop. Use only the very best oil, preferably cold pressed vegetable oil. And because you want to taste the herbal aroma, it should not be very flavoursome.

Transfer the chopped herbs or whole sprigs into the bottle and top up with the oil taking care to cover the plant completely. Close tight and leave to steep in a bright place for approx. 3 weeks. Give a good shake every now and then so that the aromatic ingredients get distributed in the viscous oil.

It is best not to make more than ½ l/1 pint of herbal oil because fresh herbs will go off after a relatively short amount of time – especially once they start being exposed to air. If you want to keep your oil for longer, you should transfer the oil to a different, preferably dark, bottle and remove all herb remnants.

Basic recipe

4 tbs chopped herbs, fresh
or 3–4 fresh sprigs
of any of the following:
basil,
summer savory,
oregano,
peppermint,
rosemary,
sage,
thyme or
hyssop

½ l/1 pint vegetable oil

clean, resealable glass bottle

TOP TIP | *Why don't you marinate Italian Antipasti using your home made herbal oils? Thyme oil goes really well with aubergines, peppers or olives.*

Herb Jelly

Basic recipe

4 tbsp fresh or 3 tbsp dried herbs
of any of the following:
basil,
tarragon,
chamomile,
lavender (flowers also go well),
peppermint,
rosemary,
thyme,
lemon balm

¾ l/1 ½ pints of apple juice

juice from 1 lemon

1 kg/2 lbs preserving sugar

Making a jelly is a lesser known method of preserving your precious herbs. You can use apple juice as a basis to cook the herbs in before you start on the jelly proper. Give it a try and surprise yourself, family and friends.

Chop the herbs and transfer to the apple juice. Leave to steep overnight.

The next day, bring everything to the boil. Take off the heat and pass the mixture through a sieve. However, it is quite possible to keep the herbs if you so wish.

Add a little lemon juice and preserving sugar to your apple juice and herb mixture and continue to cook for 1 to 4 minutes (refer to instructions).

Transfer to resealable glasses while still hot and turn over for approx. 5 minutes.

TOP TIP | *If you use delicate plants such as basil, it is best to make a strong tea first and to add this to the apple juice. Because of the extra liquid, you may have to adjust the recipe to keep the liquid to sugar ratio as instructed on the packet.*

Herb Syrup

TOP TIP | *The decoration of your herbal lemonade does not only look pretty but also adds more of that lovely aroma.*

A lemonade made from herb syrup is not only a refreshing and healthy way of quenching your thirst but will also raise an approving eyebrow or two.

Transfer the water and sugar into a large pot and bring everything to the boil. Stir frequently until all the sugar has dissolved.

Add the chopped herbs to the sugary water and stir well. Cover and leave to steep for approx. 24 hours.

Pass through a sieve, add the citric acid and leave to steep for a further 24 hours. Rinse some bottles with boiling water before pouring in the mixture.

Basic recipe

500 g/1 lb fresh herbs such as:
chamomile,
lavender,
peppermint,
burnet saxifrage,
rosemary or
lemon balm

3 l/6 pints of water

3 kg/6 lbs of sugar

resealable bottles

Herbal Salt

TOP TIP | *You can use herbal salt just as you would normal salt. But be careful: once you have added it to your dish, there is no need to add further salt.*

Basic recipe

5 parts of freshly chopped herbs
(any of the following):
dill,
lovage,
laurel,
parsley,
burnet saxifrage,
rosemary
or thyme

1 part sea salt

clean, resealable containers

This method of preserving herbs was a favourite of old and has almost been lost over time. The best herbs for making herb salt are dill, lovage, parsley and burnet saxifrage. But do not let this inhibit your fantasy, feel free to have a go at your own mixtures:

Chop the herbs finely and transfer them together with the salt to a suitable container. Arrange in layers. The ratio of herbs to salt should approx. roughly 5 to 1.

Close the container tightly and store in a dark place.

Herb Wine

Herb wines were a favourite during the Middle Ages and more than one delicious recipe was cooked up behind monastery walls. The basic ingredient are usually dry wines, white or red, as well as selected herbs. Herb wines are reduced to having one herb as their flavouring ingredient – mixtures are rather uncommon but possible. You are sure to find your favourite tipple before long.

Transfer the finely chopped herbs to a bottle (you may want to use a funnel) and top up with wine.

Put in the cork, transfer to a sunny location and leave to steep for a few days (rosemary requires 2 to 3 days, woodruff and wormwood only 1 day). You will notice that the herbs will sink to the bottom. Because of this, you should give the bottle a little shake once a day. When done, filter the wine and transfer to a different bottle. Herb wines will keep for at least 1 year.

Basic recipe for 1 1/2 pints of herb wine

2–3 tbsp fresh herbs such as:
basil,
chamomile,
lavender,
dandelion,
peppermint,
rosemary,
sage,
thyme,
woodruff (1 tbsp),
wormwood (1 tbsp) or
lemon balm

1 1/2 pints dry white or red wine

clean, resealable bottles

TOP TIP | *Use a light wine for herbs with a delicate aroma and conversely a heavier one for robuster herbs.*

73

Herbal Liqueur

TOP TIP | *Depending on how much sugar you add to your recipe, you will end up either with herbal schnapps or a liqueur.*

Basic recipe for
1 bottle of 0.7–1 l/1 ½–2 pints

5–8 tbsp freshly chopped herbs,
3–4 sprigs or 100–200 g/3 ½–7 oz
seeds or flowers of any of the following:
anise, ramson, basil,
chamomile, coriander, caraway,
lovage, dandelion,
peppermint, rosemary, sage,
thyme, lemon balm

schnapps or vodka (38–42 % vol.)

200 g/7 oz rock candy

resealable bottles

Alcohol is an excellent agent to unlock the essential oils contained in herbs – little wonder then that herbal liqueurs belong to our favourite aperitifs or digestifs. The following recipe for peppermint liqueur is supposed to get you going. Again, feel free to try out your own concoctions.

Transfer 5 tablespoons of peppermint leaves, 2 tablespoons of lemon balm, 1 tablespoon of crushed coriander seeds and the sugar to a container and top up with schnapps.

Close tightly and transfer to a warm but not too bright spot. Leave to steep for approx. 8 weeks. Give it a good shake every now and then.

Filter the liquid through a coffee filter. Rinse a bottle with boiling water before filling it with the liqueur right to the rim. Close tightly and return to a dark place. Leave to steep at room temperature for a further 8 weeks.

You can add some green food colouring to intensify the colour of your liqueur.

In the Kitchen

Green Flavours for Every Palate

Herbs in the kitchen guarantee a richness in flavour, add that certain something to any dish and, more often than not, form the basis of a tasty sauce or marinade. If used fresh, they can enthuse the palate with the whole richness of their flavour. Apart from those native to our shores, these days we have at our disposal a whole range of exotic herbs – and they are getting more popular by the minute. Fresh coriander, for example, a favourite of both the Asian and South American cuisine, is a common occurrence nowadays. The same can be said about lemon grass, which has invaded European pots and pans through Thai cooking.

Herbs in the Kitchen – a Few Basic Rules

There are some basic rules when it comes to using herbs which everyone should follow to ensure that none of that taste is wasted:

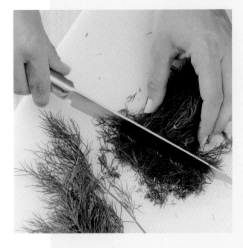

- If possible, always use fresh herbs. This is the only way to ensure that you get the full aroma.
- Always rinse herbs under the tap with a little cold water before giving them a shake or dabbing them dry with a clean kitchen towel.
- The best way of cutting large quantities of herbs is using a special mincing knife. Failing that, use a large, heavy knife with a smooth blade. Pestle and mortar may be your first choice for garlic and "hard herbs" such as rosemary or thyme.
- It is not a good idea to place herbs into a glass of water. They are not flowers and you will notice that the leaves will start drooping relatively quickly and the stems begin to rot. A much better idea is to transfer them into a freezer bag and then into the fridge. Alternatively wash, dry and chop your herbs before storing them in special containers in your freezer.
- Herbs which you add to ready-made soups or sauces should be chopped very finely. This does not hold for salads, however. Here the herbs benefit from being chopped not as finely.
- Not all herbs go with one another. If the aroma is very strong, they will start competing against each other, if it is very much alike, they will neutralise each other. Be careful when dealing with bitter herbs, less is more!
- Some herbs such as thyme and bay leaves are cooked with the other ingredients. Others such as watercress or parley are added afterwards.

Please check the table on the opposite page for information on what each herb tastes like, which herbs go with which dish, and which other herbs they harmonise with.

Wort	Taste	Use for	Notes	Goes with
wild garlic Allium ursinum	reminiscent of garlic, aromatic, slightly hot	salads, vegetables, soups, curd cheese, herb butter, risotto	use only when fresh	chives, nettles
basil Ocimum basilicum	spicy aromatic, strong taste, slightly bitter	Mediterranean cuisine, antipasti, salads, all tomato dishes	use only when fresh, basic ingredient for pesto and many bitter liqueurs	oregano, dill, chives, thyme, rosemary, chervil
borage Borgao officiales	reminiscent of cucumber	cucumber salad, lettuce, yoghurt, fish, meat and bean dishes	edible pretty flowers, the plant can also be used as a spinach substitute	summer savory, watercress, dill, chervil, tarragon, common sorrel
dill Anethom gravolens	aromatic and fresh, hint of anise, pleasantly sweet	fish, seafood, egg dishes, curd cheese, cucumber, white sauces, herb butter	use only when fresh, the seed carrying umbels can be cooked	chives, basil, parsley, watercress
tarragon Artemisia dracunulus	sweet, aromatic, hint of pepper, reminiscent of anise	fish, egg dishes, white meats, artichokes, asparagus, cauliflower, white sauces	best when fresh, do not cook, freeze	rosemary, thyme, small burnet, watercress, borage, chervil
chervil Anthriscus cerefolium	sweetish, reminiscent of anise	green sauces, soups, curd cheese, young vegetables, omelettes, grilled fish	part of the "Fines Herbs", connoisseur's parsley	parsley, chives, sage, watercress
coriander Coriandrum sativum	mild, peppery, reminiscent of curry and nutmeg	Asian cuisine, poultry, prawns, salads, light sauces, soups	kind of Asian parsley, seeds are main ingredient of curry	thyme, parsley, peppermint, chives
bay leaves Laurus nobilis	slightly bitter	stocks, soups, cabbage dishes, fish and meat marinades, ground as sausage seasoning	only dried leaves are used, bouquet garni ingredient	caraway, thyme, rosemary
lovage Levisticum officinalis	aromatic, strong celery odour and taste, very much like maggi	pulses, stews, soups, roasts, ragouts and pies	use fresh leaves for salads, otherwise cook with other ingredients	parsley, tarragon, oregano, rosemary
oregano Oreganum vulgare	intensely aromatic, strong, slightly bitter	lamb, pork, fish, sheep's cheese, vegetables, pizza, soups, salads, pulses	use fresh leaves for salads, otherwise cook with other ingredients	thyme, rosemary, tarragon, bay leaves, garlic
parsley Petroselinum crispum	aromatic, reminiscent of celery, nutmeg	potatoes, vegetables, salads, sauces, omelettes, pies, curd cheese	best used when fresh, do not cook, basic ingredient of many herb mixes	oregano, thyme, tarragon, chervil, watercress
peppermint Mentha x piperita	fresh, cool, contains menthol	fruity desserts, salads, oriental dishes, roast lamb and mutton, tea	can be used both fresh and dried	coriander, garlic
rosemary Rosmarinus officinalis	slightly bitter, resinous, a hint of camphor	grilled meat, fish, poultry, roast potatoes, vegetables, Mediterranean cuisine	mostly added to the pot/roasting dish, use sparingly	marjoram, oregano, tarragon, basil, garlic
sage Salvia officinalis	mild to very bitter depending on the kind, aromatic	vegetables, veal, lamb, poultry, liver, grilled foods, pasta, roast potatoes, tea	can be used both fresh and dried, main ingredient of saltimbocca	rosemary, basil, chervil, oregano, hyssop
chives Allium schoenoprasum	oniony, aromatic	egg dishes, curd cheese, soups, tomatoes, shrimp, smoked fish	do not cook, only use when fresh, ideal for freezing	dill, basil, chervil, oregano
thyme Thymus vulgaris	intensely aromatic, slightly bitter	meat, grilled lamb, stews, pulses, aubergines, tomatoes, mushrooms, pizza	ingredient for both bouquet garni and herbs Provençal	oregano, rosemary, bay leaves, sage, basil, tarragon
lemon grass Cymbopogon citratus	very lemony, sweet odour	Asian cuisine, tea, sweets	favourite of Indian and Asian cuisine, especially as part of mixed herbs	garlic, coriander, chervil

Favourite Mixed Herbs

Part of the seasonings used in everyday cooking are not simply leaves, fruit, seeds or roots from a single plant, but rather a clever composition of a number of individual herbs. We are going to introduce a few of those herb mixtures that have stood the test of time and come out on top. Do not let them inhibit you; you are still free to experiment!

Green Sauce

This sauce can be considered a German classic Originally from Frankfurt, this famous "green sauce" supplies us with all the vitamins otherwise so scarce during the spring. Traditionally, it is made of seven herbs: small burnet, chervil, watercress, borage, common sorrel, parsley and chives. All of these are readily available in spring and are mixed together with onions, curd cheese, yoghurt and eggs. The resulting sauce, usually served with potatoes, is very refreshing. Do not be afraid to adapt it to your taste!

Herbs Provençal

This famous herb mixture which can be found in almost any kitchen stems from the sunny Provence. It consists of rosemary, thyme, basil, marjoram, summer savory, chervil, lovage and oregano. It goes well with pasta and rice dishes, soups or salads. Roasted in olive oil, it also makes for a tasty accompaniment to meat, fish or casseroles.

Fines Herbes

Another one of the many things that come out of France is the herb mixture "fines herbs". It can be used either fresh or dried. The classic combination comes in many forms, but is usually made from three to nine different herbs including chervil, tarragon, chives and parsley. Others are summer savory, basil, thyme, sage or rosemary. Those who prefer it a little different are free to experiment, of course.

Fresh "fines herbes" can be chopped finely and mixed into curd cheese dishes, salad dressings or dips the same way you would use parsley. If short cooking times are involved as is the case with omelettes, scrambled eggs, poultry as well as fish or seafood you can add "fines herbes" from the start. The taste of the herbs, which in this case may be dried, suffers a bit in freshness but gains in intensity instead.

Bouquet Garni

Another favourite of the French cuisine is the bouquet garni which is no more than a bunch of different herbs. It is added to the dish during cooking and removed prior to serving. For this reason, it often comes pre-packed in a kind of teabag. Here the taste of the herbs but not their physical presence is the idea behind the bag. After all, there may be stalks, leaves, etc., getting in the way of the smooth consistency of the dish itself.

A bouquet garni varies depending on what it is used for. For example, if you are cooking meat, you may want a selection consisting of summer savory, basil, marjoram or oregano, rosemary and sage. For stews or soups, however, a more suitable combination would be summer savory, tarragon, marjoram and thyme. The classic bouquet garni is a mixture of parsley, thyme and bay leaves and can be used, among others, for soups or sauces.

Famous Salsas

The word "salsa" is Spanish for sauce, stock or a special kind of "hot sauce". A salsa is, therefore, always a sauce, but no two salsas are ever the same. Depending on which country the recipe comes from, you will encounter totally different combinations. We listed a few of the most famous ones below:

Salsa Verde

This is one of the most famous sauces in Mediterranean cooking. Italian parsley forms the basis for this sauce and it is complemented by – depending on where you are in the Mediterranean – capers, garlic, olive oil, salt and pepper. White bread thickens it a little and other optional ingredients include anchovies, hard-boiled eggs, pickled gherkins or pepperonis.

Pesto

A lot of fresh basil and the very best olive oil form the basis of any pesto sauce. Further ingredients of the original salsa include pine kernels, Parmesan cheese, garlic, salt and pepper. Transfer everything into a pestle and mortar and ground to a paste. This sauce, originally from Liguria, is a favourite of all pasta lovers the world over, but also goes well with boiled vegetables, grilled meat, poultry and fish and, of course, virtually every type of pasta money can buy.

Guacamole

Guacamole hails from Mexico. This creamy, thick sauce consists of an avocado puree seasoned with chili peppers, onions, tomatoes and a lot of fresh coriander. In Tex-Mex cuisine, Guacamole is the classic accompaniment for tortillas, nachos and tacos.

Avocado 'n Lemon Dip with Coriander

TOP TIP *An aromatic, light white wine or a nice cold Mexican beer – when in Rome do as the Romans – goes very well with this dip.*

Serves 4

2 avocados

juice from 2 lemons

6 spring onions

2 green chillies

a few sprigs of coriander

1 tbsp olive oil

150 g/5 oz sour cream

salt and pepper

Preparation time: approx. 15 minutes (plus 20 minutes cooling time)

Halve the avocados and remove the stone before you peel off the skin. Sprinkle some lemon juice onto the avocado immediately to prevent the flesh from turning brown.

Wash, peel and finely chop the onions. Wash the chillies and remove the seeds. Transfer to the mixer together with the spring onions.

Wash the coriander and shake dry before placing it in the blender. Give everything a good whirl, adding the oil and the sour cream. Season with salt and pepper. Cover and place in the refrigerator to steep for no less than 20 minutes. Put cling film onto the surface to prevent the dip from discolouring. Serve with tortillas, nachos or raw vegetables.

Baked Mushrooms with Mint

Clean the mushrooms thoroughly, washing them if necessary. Leave to dry. Chop larger mushrooms into bite-sized pieces. Sprinkle with approx. 1 tablespoon of lemon juice. Peel and finely chop both the garlic and the shallot.

Heat the olive oil in a frying pan and fry the mushrooms. Repeat if they do not all fit into the pan in one go. Place aside and fry the garlic and shallot. Pour in the rest of the lemon juice.

Stir in the diced tomato and tomato paste. Season everything with salt and pepper and leave to cook for approx. 2 minutes. Add the mushrooms, cover and simmer for 10 minutes.

Wash the mint and shake dry. Pluck the leaves off the sprigs and cut finely. Skewer the mushrooms onto wooden sticks, sprinkle with the mint and serve in the frying pan.

Serves 4

750 g/1 lb 11 oz oyster mushrooms
or field mushrooms
juice from 1 lemon
2 garlic cloves
1 shallot
4 tbsp olive oil
1 small tomato, diced
1 tbsp tomato paste
freshly ground black pepper
salt
2 sprigs of fresh mint

Preparation time: approx. 30 minutes

Basil Tart

Serves 8

Dough:

200 g/7 oz flour

salt

1 egg

150 g/5 oz butter

1 pinch of baking powder

Topping:

2 bunches of basil

100 ml/3 ½ fl oz cream

1–2 garlic cloves

300 g/11 oz cream cheese

200 g/7 oz full fat curd cheese

6 eggs

salt and pepper

butter to grease the form

12 halved cherry tomatoes

2 tbsp grated cheddar cheese

Preparation time: approx. 1 ½ hours

Add a pinch of salt, the egg, the cold, flaked butter and the baking powder to the flower and knead into a smooth dough. Cover and put in a cold place for approx. 30 minutes. Preheat the oven to 200 °C/390 °F/gas mark 6.

To make the topping, wash the basil and shake dry. Transfer to a blender, pour in the cream and give everything a good whirl. Peel and crush the garlic and add together with the cream cheese and curd cheese as well as the eggs. Season with salt and pepper.

Take ²⁄₃ of the dough, roll out and place into a pregreased spring form. Use the rest of the dough to make a rim some 4 cm/1 ½ inches high.

Spread the topping onto the base. Place the tart into the oven at 200 °C/390 °F/gas mark 6 for approx. 30 minutes or until golden brown. Top with the halved tomatoes and cheese 5 minutes before the end. Cut the tart into portions and serve while still warm.

Vegetable and Wild Garlic Tempura

Melt the butter in a pan and fry the vegetables. Add 200 ml/ 7 fl oz of vegetable stock, sugar and saffron and bring to the boil. Turn down the heat, cover and continue to cook for approx. 3–4 minutes until the vegetables are al dente.

Transfer the vegetables to a sieve making sure not to lose any of the stock. Pour about ⅓ of the stock into a pot, add the cream and reduce. Whisk in a yolk and stir in the vegetables. Cover and store in a cool place for approx. 2 hours. Then transfer the mixture onto the marigold leaves, fold up and make into little balls before covering them with flour.

Bring the rest of the stock to the boil, stir in the washed herbs. Pour everything into the blender, add double cream and season with salt, pepper and nutmeg. Keep warm.

Mix together the cornflour, oil and wine and heat the fat in a frying pan. Roll the balls one after the other in the wine dough and fry until golden brown. Remove and leave to dry on a piece of kitchen roll. Serve together with the sauce while still hot.

Serves 4

75 g/2 ½ oz butter
500 g/1 lb 2 oz finely diced vegetables, for example carrots, green asparagus
300 ml/11 fl oz vegetable stock
1 pinch of sugar
1 tsp saffron powder
200 ml/7 fl oz single cream
1 egg yolk
200 g/7 oz blanched marigold leaves
1 tbsp flour
1 bunch of smooth-leaved parsley
50 g/1 ¾ oz wild garlic or chives
150 ml/¼ pint double cream
salt
pepper
nutmeg
200 g/7 oz cornflour
3 tbsp olive oil
300 ml/11 fl oz dry white win
oil for frying

Preparation time: approx. 50 minutes
(plus approx. 2 hours cooling time)

Lentil and Herb Cakes with Yoghurt Sauce

Serves 4

75 g/2 ½ oz brown lentils

175 g/6 oz bulgur

1 small cucumber

250 g/9 oz natural yoghurt

3–4 garlic cloves

1 tsp sea salt

1 onion

80 ml/2 ¾ fl oz olive oil

3 tsp cumin

2 tsp ground coriander

3 tbsp freshly chopped mint leaves

4 eggs

flour

salt and pepper

Preparation time: approx. 1 hour
(plus resting period 1 ½ hours)

Cook the lentils in 300 ml/11 fl oz water for 30 minutes. Remove from the stove and add sufficient water to cover the lentils. Add the bulgur, cover with a lid and leave to soak for 1 ½ hours. Clean and wash the cucumber. Cut in half lengthways and remove the seeds. Coarsely grate the cucumber and mix into the yoghurt. Peel the garlic and crush 2 cloves which you add to the yoghurt mixture. Season everything with salt.

Heat half the oil in the frying pan. Peel the onion and fry together with the rest of the garlic for approx. 5 minutes.

Add the cumin and coriander. Transfer into a bowl and add the lentils, mint, eggs, a little flour and sea salt. Knead until you have a nice dough. If the mixture is still too liquidy add more flour. Heat the remaining oil in a frying pan. Take enough mixture for three small cakes at a time and fry until golden brown. Remove, dab dry with a kitchen towel, season if necessary with sea salt and serve together with the cold yoghurt sauce.

TOP TIP | *A little unusual but why don't you try a dry, reasonably smooth and not too fruity white wine with your lentil and herb cakes.*

Tomato and Rocket Salad

Serves 4

500 g/1 lb 2 oz ripe tomatoes

2 packets of rocket salad

1 onion

3 tbsp aceto balsamico

6 tbsp olive oil

salt

pepper

50 g/1 ¾ oz Parmesan cheese

Preparation time: approx. 20 minutes

Wash the tomatoes, remove the green bits on top and slice. Clean and wash the rocket salad before removing any thick stalks. Cut leaves into strips.

Peel the onion and dice finely. Arrange the tomatoes, rocket salad and onions on plates.

Mix the aceto balsamico, olive oil, salt and pepper to make a dressing and pour over the salad. Grate with Parmesan cheese to taste.

TOP TIP | *The slightly peppery, spicy rocket salad gives such mild vegetables as tomatoes or beans a bit of bite.*

Greek Farmer's Salad

Clean and wash both tomatoes and peppers, dry and remove stalks and seeds. Quarter the tomatoes and slice the peppers. Transfer the vegetables into a bowl. Peel the onion and cut into rings. Peel and crush the garlic clove.

Clean, wash and dry the cucumber. Cut in half lengthways and slice into approx. ½ cm/⅕ inch thick pieces. Add the onion rings, crushed garlic and cucumber to the vegetables. Pour off excess water from the olives and add to the bowl of vegetables.

Stir the lemon juice, salt and pepper until all the salt has dissolved. Then mix in the olive oil. Season the salad dressing to taste and pour over the salad. Arrange everything on plates. Cube the feta cheese and sprinkle over the salad. Finally garnish the salad with freshly chopped oregano.

Serves 4

400 g/14 oz tomatoes

2 green peppers

1 onion

1 garlic clove

1 cucumber

16 black olives

2 tbsp lemon juice

salt and pepper

125 ml/4 ½ fl oz olive oil

250 g/9 oz feta cheese

fresh oregano

Preparation time: approx. 20 minutes

French Herb Soup

Serves 4

1 shallot

100 g/3 ½ oz spinach

150 g/5 oz common sorrel

1 bunch of celery leaves

1 bunch of watercress

1 bunch of chervil

1 bunch of smooth leaved parsley

1 ½ cucumbers

1 kg/2 ¼ lb potatoes

100 g/3 ½ oz butter

coarse sea salt

100 g/3 ½ oz flaked butter

3 tbsp crème fraîche (heavy cream)

freshly ground black pepper

Preparation time: approx. 1 hour

Peel and finely chop the shallot. Clean, wash and shake the leafy vegetables and herbs dry. Retain a few leaves of basil and chervil for garnishing later on.

Clean, wash and dry the cucumber. Cut in half lengthways and use a tablespoon to remove the seeds. Dice finely. Peel the potatoes, wash and dice into bite-sized cubes. Melt the butter in a pan and add the leafy vegetables, herbs and the diced cucumber. Cover with a lid and cook for approx. 5 minutes. Take care that the vegetables and herbs do not brown.

Pour in the water, sprinkle in the salt and add the potatoes. Cook for 25 minutes. Pass the soup through a sieve. Mix in flakes of butter and crème fraîche using a handheld blender. Season everything with salt and pepper. Garnish with the remaining basil and chervil leaves and serve.

Chicken 'n Herb Soup with Coconut Milk

Peel both the carrots and onions. Slice the carrots and finely dice the onions.

Clean, wash and shake the herbs dry before chopping them finely. Heat the butter and sweat the onions until translucent. Then add the sliced carrots, thyme, parsley, bay leaf and the chicken.

Pour in 3 l/5 ¼ pints of water, season with salt and leave to simmer for 1 hour. In the meantime, cook the rice in salted water. Put aside and leave to dry.

Remove the chicken from the soup. Skin, debone and cut the meat into bite-sized pieces. Return the skin and bones to the soup and continue to simmer for another 30 minutes. Then pass the soup through a fine sieve and remove any excess fat using a skimmer. Add both rice and meat to the soup, bring to the boil once more and then stir in the coconut milk.

Continue to simmer until it has gained a slightly thick consistency. Whisk the egg yolks and cream until frothy and fold into the soup. Take off the heat immediately, transfer to a serving bowl and garnish with a little grated nutmeg.

Serves 4

2 carrots
2 onions
1 bunch of thyme
1 bunch of parsley
40 g/1 ½ oz butter
1 bay leaf
1 whole chicken
salt
125 g/4 ½ oz rice
250 ml/9 fl oz coconut milk
2 egg yolks
200 ml/7 fl oz cream
grated nutmeg

Preparation time: approx. 2 hours

Potato Wedges

TOP TIP | *Potato wedges are a favourite snack to fight off a hunger attack or to serve as an ideal accompaniment to grilled meat dishes.*

Thoroughly clean and wash the potatoes before cutting them into eight wedges each. Cook in a pot for approx. 10 minutes, remove and leave to cool.

In the meantime, take the herbs and place into a bowl together with the paprika powder, ground chillies, grated cheese, salt and flour. Peel the garlic and crush into the bowl. Mix the ingredients well. Add the slightly cooled potato wedges and give everything a good shake so that the seasoning mixture covers each potato wedge evenly.

Preheat the oven to 200 °C/390 °F/gas mark 6. Cover a baking tray with baking paper and place the potato wedges on it. Transfer to oven and grill for approx. 15 minutes, turning them frequently, or until the wedges are nice and crispy. Serve the potato wedges together with a yoghurt and cucumber dip or chutney.

Serves 4

1 kg/2 ¼ lb large potatoes

2 tsp paprika powder

1 tsp ground chillies

3 tbsp grated hard cheese, for example Cheddar

2 tsp chopped rosemary and thyme

1 tsp coarse salt

2 tbsp flour

1 garlic clove

Preparation time: approx. 30 minutes

Green Asparagus with Lemony Herb Sauce

Serves 4

1 kg/2 ¼ lb green asparagus

salt

1 large egg

1 tbsp hot mustard

200 ml/7 fl oz nut oil

juice from ½ a lemon

pepper

mixed herbs (for example chives,
chervil, tarragon)

Preparation time: approx. 35 minutes

Wash the asparagus, peel the lower third and cut off the bottom bits. Bring some water to the boil, add a little salt and cook the asparagus with the lid on for approx. 15 minutes. Remove and keep warm.

Separate the egg and put the egg white to one side. Whisk the egg yolk and mustard until frothy. Stirring continuously, slowly add the oil drop by drop.

Continue to whisk until you have a thick mayonnaise.

Add salt and pepper and season with the lemon juice. Wash the herbs and shake dry. Pluck the leaves off the stalks and chop finely.

Whisk the egg white until stiff and fold under the mayonnaise. Arrange the asparagus on plates, pour over the sauce and garnish with the freshly chopped herbs. Serve.

Courgettes with Mint and Parsley

Preheat the oven to 200 °C/390 °F/gas mark 6. Clean, wash and slice the courgettes. Peel and finely chop both the shallots and garlic cloves.

Transfer the flour to a bowl and cover the courgette slices with it. Heat 2 tablespoons of olive oil in a frying pan and fry the courgettes until golden brown. Remove and put aside.

Wash the herbs and shake dry. Chop finely. Heat the remaining oil in a frying pan and add the shallots, garlic, tomatoes including juice and herbs, keeping half of the parsley back for garnishing later on. Fry for approx. 3 minutes before seasoning everything quite strongly with salt and pepper. Remove the frying pan from the heat.

Grease an oven proof casserole dish. Line with half of the courgette slices and sprinkle with a little lemon juice. Top with the contents of the frying pan and crown with the rest of the courgette slices. Finally sprinkle with the remaining lemon juice.

Mix together the cheese and breadcrumbs and sprinkle over the oven proof dish. Transfer to the oven and cook for approx. 20 minutes. Remove, sprinkle with the rest of the parsley and serve.

TOP TIP | *The small (not longer than 15–20 cm/ 6–8 inches) courgettes have a specially delicate taste, while larger courgettes are more suitable for soups, etc.*

Serves 4

4 courgettes
2 shallots
2 garlic cloves
2 tbsp flour
4 tbsp olive oil
1 hand full of fresh mint leaves
1 bunch of smooth-leaved parsley
400 g/14 oz tinned tomatoes
salt, pepper
juice from 1 lemon
2 tbsp breadcrumbs
2 tbsp freshly grated Pecorino

Preparation time: approx. 30 minutes (plus baking time)

Rigatoni al Pesto

TOP TIP *Connoisseurs would recoil in horror if you washed basil leaves. They do, however, insist on plucking only the best leaves off the plant.*

Serves 4

3 tbsp pine kernels

3 garlic cloves

1 large bunch of basil

50 g/1 ¾ oz freshly grated

Parmesan cheese

100 ml/3 ½ fl oz olive oil

salt

400 g/14 oz rigatoni

Preparation time: approx. 30 minutes

Carefully roast the pine kernels in a frying pan without adding any fat before chopping them finely. Then peel and finely chop the garlic cloves. Wash the basil and shake dry or follow our top tip above. Cut using a mincing knife.

Mix together the pine kernels, garlic, basil and Parmesan cheese and slowly add the olive oil. Stir until you have a reasonably smooth paste. Season with salt.

Cook the pasta in salty water until al dente. Drain, hold under running cold water and shake off any excess water. Transfer to a preheated pot and mix in the pesto. Stir well to ensure that the pasta is evenly coated. Distribute on plates and serve.

Ravioli with Green Sauce

Wash and dry the meat. Heat 4 tablespoons of olive oil in a frying pan and fry the meat on all sides. Season with salt and pepper. Add the vegetables together with the onions, 3 garlic cloves, bay leaves, thyme and tomato puree. After a while, add the Marsala wine and continue to simmer for approx. 1 hour.

Mix together the flour, eggs, 2 tablespoons of oil and 1 teaspoon of salt to make a pasta dough. Cover with a moist cloth and leave to rest for approx. 30 minutes. To make the sauce, wash the herbs and transfer to a blender together with 1 garlic clove, capers, anchovies, pine kernels, 2 egg yolks, vinegar and the rest of the oil. Give everything a good whirl and season well.

Cut the meat into small pieces and cook in a little stock. Leave to reduce before taking it off the heat. Leave to cool. Mix in the breadcrumbs and Parmesan cheese. Roll the dough into two wafer thin oblongs. Place small spoonfuls of the mixture onto one oblong, brushing the intermittent areas with the rest of the egg yolk. Take the second oblong and cover the first, pressing it down between the mounds of mixture. Cut out the ravioli. Cook in salted water for 4 minutes, drain and serve with the green sauce.

Serves 4

500 g/1 lb 2 oz veal

11 tbsp olive oil

salt and pepper

1 carrot, diced

2 onions, diced

1 tomato, diced

4 chopped garlic cloves

3 bay leaves

½ tsp fresh thyme leaves

1 tbsp tomato puree

400 ml/14 fl oz Marsala wine

400 g/14 oz flour

4 eggs

1 bunch each of parsley and basil

1 tbsp capers

1 anchovy fillet (from a jar)

½ tbsp pine kernels

3 egg yolks

1 tbsp vinegar

1 tbsp breadcrumbs

1 tbsp grated Parmesan cheese

Preparation time: approx. 1 ¼ hours

Gnocchi in Sage and Gorgonzola Sauce

Serves 4

1 kg/2 ¼ lb potatoes

250 g/9 oz flour, salt

200 g/7 oz Gorgonzola cheese

1 onion

1 garlic clove

8 sage leaves

1 tbsp olive oil

300 ml/11 fl oz cream

100 ml/3 ½ fl oz dry white wine

pepper

Preparation time: approx. 50 minutes

Wash the potatoes thoroughly. Do not peel. Cook for approx. 25 minutes or until done. Drain and leave to dry. Peel and mash with a potato masher or a fork. Leave to cool a little, mix in the flour and season with salt. Knead well. Make walnut sized, oval shapes from the dough, using a fork to flatten each one, leaving a decorative imprint of its prongs. Sprinkle flour on a baking tray. Place gnocchis on the tray and leave to rest for approx. 15 minutes.

Cut the rind off the Gorgonzola and cut into small cubes. Peel and finely chop the onions and the garlic clove. Wash, dry and thinly slice the lettuce leaves.

Heat the oil in a frying pan and sweat the onion and garlic until translucent. Pour in the wine and cream and leave to reduce a touch. Add the sage and Gorgonzola and slowly melt the cheese, stirring continuously. Season the sauce with salt and pepper.

Bring a large pot of water to the boil, add the gnocchi and cook for approx. 5 minutes or until they rise to the surface. Remove with a skimmer, leave to dry and serve with the sauce.

TOP TIP | *A light dry white wine goes well with Gnocchi and sage. Ideally you should serve the same wine you used to make the Gorgonzola cheese sauce.*

Chicken Liver with Thyme and Sherry

Clean, wash and dry the chicken liver. Peel and finely dice the shallots. Heat the oil in a large frying pan and fry the liver for approx. 5 minutes or until it is brown on the outside and still slightly pink on the inside. Take care to stir carefully all the time to avoid it from sticking to the pan. Remove and keep warm.

Pour both the vinegar and the sherry into the frying pan and bring to the boil. Loosen any sticky bits from the base of the pan with a wooden spoon and stir into the mixture. Wash the thyme and shake dry before adding it to the frying pan.

Pour in the chicken stock and honey, and mix in well. Bring to the boil and continue to simmer until everything is reduced to approx. 4 tablespoons. Remove the sprig of thyme and transfer the liver back into the frying pan. Increase the flame to heat up the liver again, stirring continuously. Season everything with salt and pepper and garnish with a sprig of thyme or freshly chopped parsley.

Serves 4

350 g/12 oz chicken liver

3 small shallots

1 ½ tbsp olive oil

2 tbsp sherry vinegar

2 tbsp dry sherry

1 sprig of fresh thyme

200 ml/7 fl oz chicken stock

2 tsp honey

salt and pepper

possibly freshly chopped parsley

Preparation time: approx. 45 minutes

Chicken and Herb Fry

Serves 4

1 chicken, cleaned and gutted

(approx. 1.2 kg/2 ⅔ lb)

salt and pepper

300 g/11 oz tomatoes

1 onion

5 tbsp olive oil

150 ml/¼ pint dry white wine

1 dried chilli pepper

1 tbsp freshly chopped parsley

1 tbsp freshly chopped lovage

1 tbsp freshly chopped basil

50 g/1 ¾ oz Provolone cheese

Preparation time: approx. 1 ½ hours

Season the chicken with salt and pepper and divide into 8 pieces. Pour boiling water over the tomatoes and skin. Cut out the green stalky top and deseed before cutting them into 8 wedges each. Peel the onions and cut into rings.

Heat the oil in a frying pan and fry the chicken pieces on all sides until golden brown. Add the onion rings and continue to cook. Pour in the dry white wine and crumble in the dried chilli.

Bring everything to the boil and continue to simmer until almost all of the wine has disappeared. Now add both the tomato wedges and the herbs.

Cook the chicken for approx. 1 hour on a medium heat, making sure that the frying pan is covered. After approx. 40 minutes dice the Provolone cheese and add to the pan. When finished, taste the dish and season with salt and pepper if necessary. Serve.

Saltimbocca alla Romana

Tenderise the meat until it is quite flat. Wash and shake dry the sage leaves. Top each veal escalope with one sage leaf and one slice of ham. Secure them with a wooden toothpick.

Melt the clarified butter or ghee in a frying pan and fry the saltimbocca from both sides for 4 minutes each. Remove from the pan and keep warm.

Pour the wine into the frying pan and mix with the meat juices. Add the meat stock and bring to the boil. Reduce by a third and season with salt and pepper. Arrange the saltimbocca on plates and pour over the sauce. Serve with pasta.

Serves 4

4 veal escalopes (125 g/4 ½ oz each)
4 large sage leaves
4 slices of cured ham
(like Parma or Serrano ham)
2 tbsp clarified butter or ghee
3 tbsp dry white wine
125 ml/4 ½ fl oz meat stock
salt and pepper

Preparation time: approx. 30 minutes

Fillet of Beef with Herbs

Serves 4

1 bunch of parsley

1 sprig of tarragon

4 sage leaves

3 tbsp freshly grated Parmesan cheese

50 g/1 ¾ oz breadcrumbs

salt and pepper

75 g/2 ½ oz Pecorino cheese

1 kg/2 ¼ lb fillet of beef

150 g/5 oz cured ham

3 tbsp olive oil

2 sprigs of oregano

100 ml/3 ½ fl oz dry red wine

Preparation time: approx. 1 ¼ hours

Wash the herbs and shake dry. Pluck the tarragon leaves off the stalks. Chop the parsley, two sage leaves and the tarragon. Add the Parmesan cheese and breadcrumbs and mix well. Finally season with salt and pepper.

Slice the Pecorino cheese. Take a sharp knife and make diagonal incisions in the meat. Fill with the Parmesan cheese mixture and the slices of Pecorino. Slice the ham and wrap around the meat. Secure with pieces of string.

Preheat the oven to 180 °C/360 °F/gas mark 4 (fan assisted 160 °C/320 °F/gas mark 3). Heat the oil in a roasting tin and add the rest of the sage leaves and oregano sprigs. Then fry the meat from all sides. Transfer to the oven and roast for approx. 35 minutes. Remove the roast from the oven. Put the meat on a rack and leave to rest for approx. 10 minutes.

Place the roasting tin on the stove, pour in the wine and a little water and dissolve the meat juices while stirring continuously. Pass through a sieve and transfer to a pot. Bring to the boil. Slice the meat and serve with the sauce.

TOP TIP | *Finely chopped herbs are a favourite stuffing for meat or fish. No wonder, because their delicate flavours can really seep into every pore during cooking or roasting.*

Beef with Lemon Grass

Transfer the tamarind puree into a bowl and pour in 150 ml/ ¼ pint of hot water. Slice the meat into thin strips. Clean, wash and dry the spring onions before cutting them into thin rings. Peel and finely chop the garlic cloves. Peel the ginger and grate finely. Clean the lemon grass and remove the outer leaves. Wash and dry and chop the lower bits very finely.

Mix together the tamarind puree and the water before passing it through a sieve, making sure to catch all the juices. Mash the shrimp paste with a fork.

Heat the oil in a wok. Add the spring onion rings, putting a few aside for later use, the garlic, lemon grass and ginger and stir fry for approx. 3 minutes. Move to one side and add the strips of meat. Fry on a high heat from all sides for approx. 10 minutes or until golden brown and cooked.

Pour the soy sauce to the tamarind juice and add to the rest of the ingredients. Cook for a further 10 minutes, stirring every now and then. Season a little with salt, garnish with the rest of the spring onion rings and serve with rice.

INFO | *Lemon grass is a favourite in the Southeast Asian cuisine. The long stalks of this plant with a bulbous root are not dissimilar to spring onions, but a lot harder.*

Serves 4

1 tbsp tamarind puree
750 g/1 ¾ lb rump of beef
½ bunch of spring onions
2 garlic cloves
1 piece of fresh ginger
(approx. 4 cm/1 ½ inches)
2 stalks fresh lemon grass
½ tsp shrimp paste
2 tbsp sweet soy sauce
3 tbsp coconut oil
salt

Preparation time: approx. 45 minutes

Lamb Ragout with Mushrooms and Rosemary

Serves 4

1 kg/2 ¼ lb boned leg of lamb

500 g/1 lb 2 oz small field mushrooms

200 g/7 oz onions

3 tbsp olive oil

125 ml/4 ½ fl oz dry white wine

salt

pepper

1 tbsp freshly chopped rosemary

2 tbsp Marsala wine

Preparation time: approx. 1 ½ hours

Take a sharp knife and dice the leg of lamb. Clean the mushrooms and wipe with a wet cloth. Peel and chop the onions.

Preheat the oven to 190 °C/375 °F/gas mark 5 (fan assisted 170 °C/340° F/gas mark 4). Heat the oil in an ovenproof dish and fry the meat from all sides. Add the onions, stirring frequently. When translucent, add the mushrooms, pour in the wine and top up with enough water to fully cover the meat. Season with salt, pepper and rosemary.

Put on the lid and transfer the dish to the oven. Roast the ragout for approx. 1 hour or until the meat is nice and soft. Season with Marsala wine and serve with a fresh French stick.

Lamb Cutlets with Salsa Verde

Wash the lemons using hot water, dry and grate the zest before squeezing out the juice. Mix together 1 teaspoon of zest, 2 teaspoons of lemon juice, 2 tablespoons of oil and the mustard. Marinade the meat in the mixture for 4 hours.

To make the salsa, wash the parsley and shake dry. Transfer to a blender and add the anchovies, the rest of the lemon zest and 1 tablespoon of lemon juice. Blend until smooth. Peel and crush the garlic and add. Pour in 2 tablespoons oil. Give everything a good stir, cover and leave for 2 hours for the flavours to develop.

Preheat the oven to 200 °C/390 °F/gas mark 6 (fan assisted 160 °C/320 °F/gas mark 3). Remove the meat from the marinade and fry in 1 tablespoon of oil. Transfer to the oven and continue to cook for approx. 15 minutes or until the meat is tender. Arrange the meat on a platter and serve together with the salsa verde and the drained capers.

Serves 4

2 lemons
5 tbsp olive oil
1 tbsp mustard
4 lamb cutlets
1 bunch of parsley
3 anchovies
2 garlic cloves
2 tbsp small capers

Preparation time: approx. 30 minutes (plus marinading time of 4 hours, salsa has to rest for 2 hours)

Wild Boar Herb Medallions

Serves 4

1 small onion

3–4 garlic cloves

3 tbsp olive oil

125 ml/4 ½ fl oz red wine

2 tbsp freshly chopped thyme and rosemary each

2 juniper berries

1 leek

800 g/1 ¾ lb thick slices of wild boar fillet

1 small fresh pineapple

1 tsp each of oil, pepper, salt, mustard

4 rashers of streaky bacon

Preparation time: approx. 45 minutes
(plus marinading time 24 hours)

Peel and finely chop both the onion and the garlic cloves. Mix together with the olive oil, red wine, herbs and the juniper berries.

Pour the marinade into a shallow dish. Clean, wash and slice the leek. Transfer to the marinade, add the meat and leave to steep for 24 hours.

Peel the pineapple, remove the stalky top and cut into thick slices. Brush the pineapple slices with oil and sprinkle all over with coarsely ground pepper.

Remove the boar from the marinade and season with salt and pepper. Brush mustard onto the medallions and wrap in the streaky bacon. Transfer to a hot grill and cook for approx. 6–10 minutes in total.

Transfer the peppered slices of pineapple onto the grill and cook on each side for approx. 3 minutes. Serve together.

Scallops Provençal

TOP TIP | *Fresh and fruity, uncomplicated dry white wines which are reasonably acidic make for an ideal accompaniment to fish or seafood.*

Pour boiling water over the tomatoes, hold them quickly under the running cold tap and skin. Then halve, deseed and dice them. Peel and finely dice the onions and shallots before frying them in 2 tablespoons of olive oil for 5 minutes. Pour in the wine, cook a little and add the tomatoes. Season with salt and pepper and continue to cook for another 20 minutes or until the sauce has thickened a little.

Preheat the oven to 200 °C/390 °F/gas mark 6. Heat the rest of the oil and butter, turn up the flame and fry the scallops on all sides for 1–2 minutes or until golden brown. Put to one side. Peel and crush the garlic and transfer to the hot frying pan. Fry for about 1 minute. Take the frying pan off the heat and add the herbs and breadcrumbs.

Heat the scallop shells in the oven at 200 °C/390 °F/gas mark 6. Put a little tomato sauce in each hot shell, followed by a scallop. Sprinkle with the breadcrumb mixture and serve immediately.

Serves 4

600 g/1 ¼ lb very ripe tomatoes

1 onion

4 shallots

3 tbsp olive oil

75 ml/2 ½ fl oz white wine

salt and pepper

2 tbsp butter

20 fresh, cleaned scallops

4 garlic cloves

2 tbsp freshly chopped parsley

½ tsp fresh thyme leaves

2 tbsp fresh breadcrumbs (white)

20 scallop shells

Preparation time: approx. 1 ¼ hours

Coriander Omelette with Prawns

Serves 4

250 g/9 oz fresh prawns

1 tsp salt

1 tbsp corn starch

2 spring onions

6 eggs

white pepper

½ tbsp sunflower oil

250 g/9 oz clarified butter

2 tbsp freshly chopped coriander leaves

Preparation time: approx. 45 minutes

Wash the prawns, peel and remove the black gut. Transfer to a bowl and add ½ teaspoon of salt and the corn starch. Add a little water and toss the prawns in the mixture until they are well covered from all sides. Wash the prawns once again and rub dry.

Clean the spring onions before washing and slicing them into fine rings. Crack the eggs into a bowl, season with salt and pepper, stir in the oil and mix well.

Melt the clarified butter in either a wok or a cast-iron frying pan and fry the prawns for approx. 2 minutes. Once they have turned pink remove them from the pan and place on a piece of kitchen roll to soak up any excess fat.

Pour the remaining clarified butter into a separate container, keeping only about 2 tablespoons in the pan. Reheat and fry the spring onions. Add the eggs and increase the heat slowly. Add the prawns as soon as the eggs show signs of solidifying. Continue to cook until the eggs are done and the prawns are hot.

Transfer the cooked omelettes with prawns to plates and garnish with chopped coriander leaves. Serve.

TOP TIP | *Coriander – also known as "Chinese parsley" – is one of the oldest known herbs. It is, therefore, not surprising that it is hard to imagine Asian cuisine without either its seeds or leaves.*

Fish in Red Curry Sauce

Wash and dab the fish fillet dry and cut into strips. Wash and dry the pepper, remove the stalky top, deseed, and dice. Clean and wash the spring onions and cut into 3 cm/ 1 inch long rolls. Remove the outer leaves of the lemon grass and finely chop the lower, white part of the plant.

Heat the oil in a frying pan and stir in the red curry paste, stirring continuously until it has completely dissolved. Pour in the coconut milk, oyster sauce, sugar and the lemon juice. Stir well. Now add the vegetables together with the lemon grass and bring the mixture to the boil.

Add the fish to the boiling sauce and turn down the heat. Continue to simmer for approx. 3 minutes. Transfer to plates and garnish with freshly chopped coriander leaves. Rice makes for an ideal accompaniment to this dish.

Serves 4

500 g/1 lb 2 oz ocean perch fillets

1 red pepper

3 spring onions

1 stalk of lemon grass

1 tbsp peanut oil

2 tbsp red curry paste

400 ml/14 fl oz unsweetened coconut milk

4 tbsp oyster sauce

1 tbsp palm sugar

1 tbsp lemon juice

3 tbsp freshly chopped coriander

Preparation time: approx. 30 minutes

Fish Cakes with Dill

Serves 4

750 g/1 lb 11 oz cooked white fish,
for example cod

5 large slices of white bread

1 tomato

1 onion

1 garlic clove

3 eggs

2 tbsp chopped dill

salt and pepper

nutmeg

a little oil

Preparation time: approx. 50 minutes

Flake the cooked fish with a fork and transfer to a bowl. Cut the bread into large cubes and place in hot water to soak. Remove again and squeeze to get rid off any excess liquid.

Take the tomatoes, make a crosswise incision and pour boiling water over them. Now skin the tomatoes, deseed and dice finely. Peel and dice both the onion and the garlic clove very finely. Mix together with the bread and the diced tomatoes and add everything to the fish.

Whisk the eggs and put in the dill. Season with salt and pepper and add the final touch with grated nutmeg. Mix everything together well. Wet your hands, take a little of the mixture and form a flat cake. Continue until all the dough is used. Brush some oil onto the cakes and transfer to a hot grill – alternatively use a frying pan – and cook for approx. 3 minutes on each side. Serve hot.

TOP TIP | *In order not to be overpowered by the strong taste of this dish, you need an intense, fruity white wine which has plenty of substance and depth to stand up to the strong flavours. Our suggestion: a South African Sauvignon Blanc.*

Panna Cotta with Lemon Balm

Serves 4

4 sheets of white gelatin
250 g/9 oz cream
250 ml/9 fl oz milk
1 vanilla pod
3 tbsp sugar
2 tbsp finely chopped lemon balm
2 tbsp Marsala wine
4 lemon balm leaves

*Preparation time: approx. 30 minutes
(plus 6 hours chilling time)*

Soften the gelatine in sufficient cold water. Pour the cream and milk into a pan, cut open the vanilla pod and scrape out the seeds using a teaspoon. Add to the cream and milk mixture. Stir in the sugar and bring everything to the boil. Turn down the heat and continue to simmer for approx. 10 minutes.

Squeeze the gelatine to remove any excess liquid and add to the cream and milk mixture. Dissolve while stirring continuously. Stir in the chopped lemon balm and remove the pan from the stove.

Rinse little round dishes with cold water and pour in the Panna Cotta. Transfer to the refrigerator and chill for at least 6 hours or until it has become firm. Invert the Panna Cotta onto plates, sprinkle with Marsala wine and decorate with lemon balm leaves.

Home Medicine Chest and Cosmetics

Medicine Straight from the Garden

Whether a wort is primarily used in the kitchen or used as a medicinal plant applied in the form of tea, tincture or as an ointment largely depends on its active ingredients (please refer to pages 19 to 23). Sometimes, however, it is quite impossible to draw the line. Rosemary is a prime example in that its needles provide lamb chops with their characteristic aroma; at the same time, it is often used as an ingredient in bubble baths or as a tonic in the form of wine. Peppermint is another candidate – we know its medicinal uses mainly in the form of tea in case of an upset stomach, but it is also a wonderful ingredient in many sauces or desserts.

Manifold Uses

While the above is confusing enough, the manifold uses of some herbs do not help the situation. Sometimes one and the same wort can cure any number of ailments. Be it an upset stomach, sleeping problems or migraines – an infusion made from the leaves of lemon balm will help with any of the above. Many herbs that we know from the kitchen display not only the common qualities of stimulating both appetite and the digestive tract, but also have

antibacterial or anti-inflammatory properties: thyme or sage for example will not only ease digestion of heavy foods, but will also abate sore throats if used as a mouth wash.

The explanation for these manifold uses lies in the composition and structure of herbal agents. More often than not, we do not only deal with one but many constituents that as a unit display aforementioned properties. It is thus a complicated interplay between any number of active ingredients that help, for example, our digestion. This is also the reason why synthetically produced medicines which we know from the chemist's cannot boast of such a broad spectrum of possible applications as that of a medicinal plant. Contrary to medicine as we know it, naturotherapy does not rely on specific active ingredients, be they isolated or even produced synthetically. To this day, the interaction between different agents has not been fully understood even though a lot of research has gone into the matter.

Healthy and Fit – Thanks to Herbal Medicine

Herbs play an important part in both medicine and preventative measures, a fact which is true for all cultures and all times. There really is a wort for every ailment. There is the proviso, however, that "green" medicine is always the first choice for the less serious ailments. Therefore, if you suffer from an upset stomach, wind, a runny nose, a sore throat or you feel a proper cold coming on, your first port of call will be the home medicine chest with its herbal preparations. Serious illnesses, high temperatures or anything to do with organs, even problems that simply do not want to go away, however, require a visit to your local GP.

Wort	Which Part	When	How
arnica Arnica montana	fully opened flowers	June to August	external use only; compressions, infusions or alcohol extract in case of aching muscles/joints or strains
chamomile Matricaria recutita	young flowers; small, tender leaves	June to August	vapour bath to treat colds; tea for upset stomach, indigestion; gurgle in case of sores in mouth/throat; for wounds that do not heal
coltsfoot Tussilago farfara	young leaves and flowers	May to June	tea for bronchitis as expectorant; anti-inflammatory; do not ingest over longer periods!
dandelion Taraxacum officinale	leaves prior to flowering, root, fully opened flower	March to April; autumn	tea for problems with liver/gall; good in spring because of cholagogue and depurative properties
fennel Foeniculum vulgare	seeds	September to October	crush and make tea against cramps combined with wind in stomach and digestive tract; expectorant in case of bronchitis or asthma; chew seeds against bad breath
lady's mantle Alchemilla xanthochlora	leaves	March to September	tea for women's ailments, menopause problems, heavy periods; also against upset stomach/digestion; depurative
lavender Lavandula angustifolia	buds that are just about to open	May to June	tea for upset stomach, loss of appetite, migraine; bubble bath in case of anxiety or sleeping problems
lemon balm Melissa officinalis	leaves and tops of shoots prior to flowering, flowers	May to October	tea, juice or bubble bath against upset stomach, sleeping problems, anxiety or migraine
marigold Calendula officinalis	fully opened flowers	June to September	as compression or ointment for wounds that refuse to heal, rashes, burns, infections
peppermint Mentha x piperita	leaves and tops of shoots prior to flowering, flowers	June to October	tea in case of nausea, stomach ache, wind, gall stones and problems with the liver; do not ingest over longer periods!
rosemary Rosmarinus officinalis	leaves and tops of shoots during/after flowering	May to September	tea for low blood pressure, dizziness and indigestion; tonic bubble bath
sage Salvia officinalis	leaves and tops of shoots prior to flowering, flowers	May to September	tea for oral infections (gurgling, too, good for vocal chords); against indigestion, wind, diarrhoea
St. John's wort Hypericum perforatum	freshly opened flowers, uppermost leaves	June to August	tea as a pick-me-up; St. John's wort oil (crushed flowers and olive oil, ratio 1:4) for wounds and abscesses; careful, sensitises skin!
thyme Thymus vulgaris	whole branches during flowering period	May to September	as tea or steam bath against dry cough, bronchitis, asthma; external: compressions against wounds, abscesses, fungal infections
valerian Valeriana officinalis	roots	September to October	tea in case of sleeping problems, anxiety, nervous stomach disorders; against acne (to clean up skin)
wormwood Artemisia absinthium	leaves and tops of shoots during flowering period	May to September	tea against loss of appetite, digestion problems, upset stomach; use sparingly, do not ingest over longer periods!
yarrow Achillea millefolium	flowering plant without roots	June to October	tea against upset stomach, digestive problems, loss of appetite; bubble bath for inflamed skin rashes; improves blood circulation, antiseptic

Applications

Medicines obtained from plants can be ingested or applied externally onto the skin in a number of different ways. In order to gain access to these valuable substances, we have a number of different options:

Herbal Teas, Extractions and Infusions...

... count among the most well known household remedies. They are also very easy to prepare. To make an extraction or infusion pour boiling hot water over the chopped leaves or flowers and leave to steep for approx. 10 minutes. You will need about 50 g/2 oz of fresh or 20 g/²⁄₃ oz of dried herbs respectively for ½ l/1 pint of water. You can add sugar or even a shot of lemon juice to season your concoction to taste. Unfortunately, these extractions do not keep for very long and they will be quite useless if stored in the fridge for more than 24 hours.

TOP TIP

Use a specially reserved pot for herbal teas as remnants of tanning agents from black tea will impair both aroma and medicinal effect.

Brews ...

... are made primarily from the roots or woody parts of the plant. To make a proper brew you need 30 g/1 oz of dried or twice the amount of fresh ingredients. Bring ½ l/1 pint of water to the boil, add the chopped herb, turn down the heat and simmer for 15 minutes. The brew can be drunk as a tea or used as part of a compression. Brews will keep for approx. 24 hours if kept in the refrigerator.

Tinctures ...

... are concentrated herb extracts in alcohol. They are ingested undiluted or added to hot drinks or can be applied externally as part of compressions or wet packs or, alternatively, added dropwise to ointments or bathing water. In order to make a tincture, you need 4 parts of high proof alcohol – a bottle of vodka is suitable – and one part of chopped herbs. Mix and leave to steep for some 2 to 3 weeks. Filter and fill into brown bottles. Store in a cool, dark place so as not to lose any of the tincture's active ingredients.

Juices...

... from herbs are gained by pressing them out using a juicer or other implement. The juice thus gained should be drunk immediately. Unfortunately, the yield is not very great, so you will need a lot of herbs to get enough juice for a single glass.

Essential oils...

... can be gained by steam distillation of chopped herbs. This method will extract the valuable oils in an extremely efficient manner and leave you with a highly concentrated viscous liquid. Essential oils are probably most famous for their use in aromatherapy, which has been exploiting the tonic and therapeutic qualities of essential oils for eons. Nearly all civilised cultures have employed herbal oils to combat both physical and emotional ailments. Essential oils can be applied externally via the skin, inhaled or even ingested.

Most home users will consider distillation probably a little bit too elaborate and expensive to contemplate. There is an easier method, even though the result will not be as concentrated as essential oils. Such a brew will, however, be very similar in all other aspects. You will need 750 g/1 ½ lbs of fresh, chopped herbs or roughly 400 g/14 oz dried herbs and ½ l/1 pint of oil – preferably with as little taste as possible (for example thistle oil). Heat the oil, add the herbs leave to simmer on a small flame for approx. 2 to 3 hours. Leave to cool, filter and transfer to brown bottles. To make a cold brew, pack the herbs into a resealable jar and top up with oil. It should cover all plant material. Close and transfer to a bright, sunny place. The cold brew will be ready to use after approx. 2 to 3 weeks. You can increase the concentration by replacing the herbs after about 1 ½ weeks.

St. John's wort oil (see above) made in such a manner will alleviate aching muscles as well as rheumatic disorders. It can also be applied to smaller wounds to help and speed up the healing process. Oil made from lavender will bolster the calming effect of a massage and is good for your nerves if inhaled.

Ointments...

... can be made by slowly heating the base (some fat based compound like Vaseline or beeswax, etc) and the herb in a bowl of water. Keep it hot for a good two hours so that the active ingredients are extracted. Filter, stir until smooth and fill into resealable jars while still warm. You will need some 60 g/2 oz of dried or 100 g/3 ½ oz of fresh herbs and approx. 500 g/1 lb of fat. Another possibility would be to add herbal oil to the base instead of herbs (please refer to page 118 for a recipe). Ointments will keep for a long time because they do not contain water (contrary to creams). If the lid is properly sealed, you should still be able to use them after a year.

To crush herbs – especially dried ones – a pestle and mortar are essential.

In Case of a Sore Throat

TOP TIP *Children will love sage honey even when they are not ill: add the juice and grated zest of one untreated lemon, 15 fresh sage leaves, 1 cinnamon stick and 5 cloves to 500 g/1 lb of honey. The ingredients can stay in the honey. It tastes delicious on bread or in herbal teas.*

For 1 mug of sage tea
you will need:

4–5 fresh sage leaves
¼ l/½ pint of water
1 tsp vinegar

For 1 mug of thyme tea
you will need:

1 sprig with fresh thyme leaves
¼ l/½ pint of water
1 tsp lemon juice

If your throat starts to hurt, you can be sure that a cold is just around the corner. The least you will get for your trouble is a sore throat: time for sage with vinegar or thyme.

Wash and shake the sage leaves before cutting them finely. Transfer to a cup and top up with boiling water. Leave to brew for approx. 10 minutes. Add 1 teaspoon of vinegar and use to gurgle. What you cannot gurgle away, can be drunk in the form of tea.

To make the thyme variety, wash a sprig of thyme and shake off excess water. Pluck off and chop the leaves. Put 1 teaspoon of chopped thyme leaves into a mug, top with boiling water and leave to brew for approx. 10 minutes. Add one teaspoon freshly squeezed lemon juice. Use some of it for gurgling and drink the rest as tea.

You can use thyme and sage infusions for throat compresses, too.

When the Stomach or Bowels Come up

Many digestion problems are caused by too much and/or wrong food. However, smaller ailments are quite easily and quickly treatable using traditional household remedies.

You need to wash, shake dry and chop the herbs. To make one mug's worth of herbal tea, you need approx. 1 teaspoon of the herb in question or the same amount of crushed seeds (see right). Top up with 200 ml/⅓ pint boiling water and leave to brew for a good 10 minutes. Strain the tea and drink in small sips. Sweeten to taste with honey – especially in the case of the bitter wormwood tea.

The best herbs in case of an upset stomach or digestive tract ...

1 tbsp per mug
depending on taste choose one
of the following:
fennel (seeds)
peppermint (leaves)
sage (leaves)
thyme (leaves)
marjoram (leaves)
rosemary (leaves)
dill (seeds)
lemon balm (leaves)
wormwood (leaves)

TOP TIP | *If you happen to have essential oils or even herbal oils at your disposal, simply add 10 drops of oil to a mug of hot water.*

Marigold Ointment for a Healthy Skin

TOP TIP | *Marigold ointment is excellent against skin imperfections (even acne), wounds that refuse to heal, eczemas, burns and other inflammations.*

You will need:

pickling jars
coffee filter
napkin (not paper)
oven-proof dish (beaker)
small saucepan
plastic spoon
pot
100 ml/3 ½ oz marigold oil with wheat germ base
15 g/ ½ oz beeswax
10 g/⅓ oz propolis, crushed finely

To make herbal oil, you will need a generous 100 g/3 ½ oz of dried, chopped flower leaves, Place them in a pickling jar. Top up with approx. 1 l/2 pints of wheat germ oil. Close and leave to steep for 3 weeks in a warm, bright place. Give it a good shake every now and then. Then strain the oil using a coffee filter. Press out the oily bits of herbs (best done with a napkin) to extract the last bits and filter. Finally pour the herbal oil in brown resealable bottles.

To make the ointment, melt beeswax in an oven-proof dish in a bath of hot water, add the marigold oil and mix in well with the melted wax. As soon as the mixture becomes homogeneous, remove from the water bath and stir until it becomes smooth. Leave to cool a little, add the propolis powder and give the mixture another good stir.

Transfer the ointment to resealable jars, leave to cool and and shut tightly.

Arnica Compressions in Case of Injuries

In case of smaller injuries, where the skin has not broken such as bruises, strains or inflammations, arnica is the ideal medicine.

To make a compression, immerse a piece of cloth such as absorbent gauze or a small towel into an infusion or extraction made from chopped up arnica flowers. Wring out and place on problem area. The compression should be very hot. Repeat once it has cooled until the pains and aches have disappeared.

To make a pack, wrap the arnica infused or in extraction immersed towel around the problem area. Another possibility is to use the fresh wort and add a little water. Then heat the mixture until it becomes pulpy. Place the pap between two layers of gauze and place directly onto the skin.

You will need:

1 piece of cloth (cotton or linen), gauze or absorbent gauze, compress
3 tbsp arnica flowers
½ l/1 pint of water

INFO | *Arnica is a protected plant and must not be collected from the wild. Careful: do not ingest, as there is a danger of poisoning!*

Completely Natural Make-up

Herbs can not only make you feel better in the way of medicine but also improve your looks! Already the ancient Egyptians, Greeks and Romans took daily baths, looked after and protected their skin with selected oils and fragrant ointments. Enriched with herbs and flowers, aromatic essences, tinctures and oil one was quite aware of and appreciated the stimulating, relaxing and all-round pampering qualities of natural cosmetics – almost a kind of aromatherapy. Most plants that can be used for cosmetics also have medicinal properties. It is therefore impossible to separate plants grown for cosmetics or medicinal usage. Not surprising, as health and a sense of well being are also inseparable.

Natural Cosmetics Do-It-Yourself

Making natural herbal cosmetics is simpler than you might think and is no different to making a cup of herbal tea. However, **always** test home-made natural cosmetics first on a sensitive piece of skin. Ideal for this is perhaps the crook of the arm or similar. People with sensitive skin may have allergic reactions. Cleanliness and good hygiene is also of absolute importance. Carefully rinse all containers and tools you are likely to use. Only use immaculate herbs. That said here are a few examples:

- Baths are an ideal way to relax and let the soul drift, to recharge those batteries and leave things behind. A herbal bath requires a handful of herbs (some 20–50 g/1–2 oz) which you put into a small bag made out of linen (10 x 20 cm/4 x 8 inches, tie up with some string). Place in the bathtub and fill with water.
- A facial tonic or perfume of some sort cleanses and refreshes the skin. Alcohol diluted with a lot of water and water based herbal essences are ideal for normal to greasy skin. Dry or sensitive skin requires herbal essences mixed with fruit or wine vinegar or oil. Alcohol and vinegar will preserve the herbal ingredients and your tonic or perfume will probably keep for a whole year.
- A herbal massage oil is not only very good for your skin but easy on the nose. Depending on the herbal essences (½ l/1 pint wheat germ oil : 50 g/2 oz fresh herb) contained in the massage oil, it will have a calming and relaxing or a vitalising and refreshing effect.
- Herbal rinses can revitalise your hair, give it new shine, intensify the colour and protect it. You will need approx. 3 tablespoons of chopped herbs. Pour over ¼ l/½ pint of boiling water. Leave to brew until it has cooled down before straining off. Pour the resulting infusion over your hair and massage your head gently. Do not rinse out.

Wort	For your Skin	In the Bath	For your Hair	As Tea
catnip Nepeta cataria	in case of irritation of the skin	for sleeping problems; against anxiety; slight diaphoretic	against dandruff; makes hair shine; against irritation of the skin	reduces fever, in case of sleeping problems or digestive problems
chamomile Matricaria recutita	cooling effect; vapour bath cleanses skin	flowers for relaxing, hip bath for inflamed vagina	rinse for blond hair; makes hair shine	in case of sleeping problems; for inflammation of nose or throat
comfrey Symphytum officinale	smooths dry skin; against skin imperfections	healing; in case of aching muscles or joints, relaxing	against dry hair; rinse for dark hair	leaves and roots against stomach ulcers and colds
dandelion Taraxacum officinale	cleans greasy skins; herbal oil against freckles or pigment faults	leaves have cleansing and healing properties; tonic	relaxing for the skin	in case of digestive problems
fennel Foeniculum vulgare	astringent for greasy skin; calming in case of inflammation	cleansing	against greasy hair; lends shine	in case of feeling unwell, place on inflamed eyes
hops Humulus lupulus	cleansing	relaxing	strengthening effect	in case of sleeping problems; slight laxative
lady's mantle Alchemilla xanthochlora	astringent for greasy skin and acne; stops blood flow	relaxing; as hip bath in case of menstruation problems or abdominal pain		in case of menstruation problems; as mouth rinse
lavender Lavandula angustifolia	vapour bath or facial tonic cleanses skin; tightens skin, antiseptic	flowers for relaxing; cleanses, deodorises	for greasy hair	in case of headaches, anxiety, sleeping problems
lemon balm Melissa officinalis	cleansing; refreshing	leaves for relaxing; against general state of anxiety		in case of headaches, sleeping problems, upset stomach, digestive problems
marigold Calendula officinalis	astringent for fatty skin; moisturises dry skin; cleansing, healing qualities	petals have cleansing qualities, astringent; good for varicose veins	as rinse for auburn hair	for upset stomach, gall problems
peppermint Mentha x piperita	astringent; calming; cleansing	leaves are stimulating, good for blood circulation	for greasy hair; dandruff	against wind, nausea, colics, gall problems; colds
rosemary Rosmarinus officinalis	cleansing, stimulating	needles are stimulating, good for blood circulation; deodorising foot bath	rinse for dark hair; against dandruff and greasy hair; lends shine	against upset stomach, weak cardiovascular system, low blood pressure
sage Salvia officinalis	antiseptic; astringent; apply fresh leaves to insect stings	calming hand bath	against dandruff; rinse for dark hair; lends shine	against coughs, sore throats, upset stomachs, good for vocal chords
stinging nettle Urtica diocia	cleansing; astringent in case of impurities	cleansing	protective; strengthening; lends shine; against dandruff	diuretic; good for purification
thyme Thymus vulgaris	cleansing; refreshing; antiseptic; as face tonic or steam bath	in case of colds	rinse for dark hair; against dandruff	against colds, upset stomach, asthma problems
violet Viola odorata	cleansing; makes skin supple; good vapour bath	against anxiety		against coughs, sore throats, expectorant
yarrow Achillea millefolium	cleansing; antiseptic; astringent, refreshing	leaves have cleansing and astringent properties		against wind, upset stomach

Herbal Steam Bath

For one herbal steam bath
you will need:

5 tbsp fresh or
3 tbsp dried herbs
1 1/2 pints hot water (not boiling)

The breathing in of healing vapour coming from a steam bath can, on the one hand help in case of colds by calming the inflamed mucous membranes and having a decongestive effect. On the other hand, such a steam bath will clean your skin, help irritable skin relax and clear up impurities.

Transfer the herb of your choice – best selected according to skin type – into a bowl, pour in the hot water and give everything a stir. Put a large towel over you head and place your face over the hot vapour – make sure to close your eyes – for approx. 5 to 10 minutes.

TOP TIP | *A steam bath made with stinging nettles or lavender cleanses the skin. Note that lavender also has a calming effect on frayed nerves.*

Herbal Milk Bath

You can just about take any oil for your herbal milk bath which you also use in the kitchen. But a beauty bath is always something special – you are treating yourself, after all. The same might as well apply to the oil. Jojoba oil, oil made from almonds or grape seed oil are ideally suited. All you need now is an emulsifying agent so that the oil is dispersed in the bath rather than floating separately on the surface. Cream will do just fine for our purposes.

Transfer the oil and cream into a small bowl and stir well. Add the herbs and mix everything well.

Fill the bath with water – the ideal bathing temperature is 29 °C/85 °F. Pour in the oil and cream mixture and disperse with expansive, generous hand movements.

You can influence the qualities of your herbal milk bath by choosing the right herb for your purposes (see page 121).

For one herbal milk bath
you will need:

2 tbsp jojobo oil (but wheat germ
oil will do as well)
200 ml/7 fl oz single cream
5 tbsp fresh or 3 tbsp dried herbs

Lavender Facial Tonic

Lavender facial tonic

Ingredients for approx.
400 ml/14 fl oz

5 tbsp fresh or 3 tbsp dried
lavender flowers
100 ml/3 ½ fl oz apple vinegar
300 ml/10 ½ fl oz distilled water

Facial tonics refresh and tighten the skin. Below is an example of a gentle tonic for all skin types which will liven up any complexion.

Place the lavender flowers into a screw-top glass. Add the vinegar and water and screw on the lid tightly. Give the mixture a good shake and leave to steep in a warm, bright place for approx. 1 week, shaking it thoroughly once a day.

At the end of the week, strain off the tonic and transfer into a suitable resealable bottle.

TOP TIP | *If you happen to be short of lavender flowers, you can make this facial tonic using lavender leaves instead.*

A–Z of Herbs

Achillea millefolium – Yarrow

Family:
Asteraceae/Compositae
(daisy family)

Also known as:
Staunchgrass, bloodwort,
carpenter's weed, milfoil

Range:
Europe

Size:
Perennial growing to 1 m/
3 foot 4 inches tall

Typical characteristics:
Aromatic perennial with
white to pink composite
flowers

Cultivation:
Full sun; rich soil;
may require staking;
remove dead flowers;
rejuvenate by dividing the
plant every 3–5 years

Yarrow is highly regarded because of its vulnerary, anti-inflammatory, digestive and calming properties. An infusion made from a flowering shoot may be used for cleaning small wounds or as a mouthwash. The plant is sometimes also used to flavour herbal liqueurs.

Alchemilla xanthochlora – Lady's Mantle

Family:
Rosaceae (rose family)

Also known as:
Lion's foot, nine hooks

Range:
Europe

Size:
Perennial growing to
40 cm/1 foot 4 inches tall

Typical characteristics:
Basal rosette of large,
mostly folded leaves

Cultivation:
Sunny to partial shade;
clayey, fresh soil;
water during dry spells;
supply with compost
in the autumn

The leaves of this sought after medicinal herb are particularly known to ease women's ailments such as excessive bleeding or cramps during menstruation. The plant's common name stems from its large overlapping leaves which supposedly resemble the mantle of Virgin Mary, mother of Jesus Christ.

Allium cepa – Onion

Family:
Alliaceae (leek family)

Also known as:
Garden onion

Range:
Western Asia

Size:
Perennial growing up to
90 cm/3 foot tall

Typical characteristics:
Large white to crimson
coloured inflorescences

Cultivation:
Sunny; well-drained,
light, rich soil;
water during dry spells;
propagation through
cuttings

Onion has been cultivated for thousands of years due to its culinary and medicinal properties. In the kitchen, it is used to add that little something to meat dishes, soups or salads. In naturopathy, it is known as an anti-inflammatory, appetising, stomachic and hypotensive agent.

• Recipe pp. 96, 109

Allium sativum – Garlic

Family:
Alliaceae (leek family)

Also known as:
Poor man's treacle

Range:
Central Asia

Size:
Perennial growing up to
1 m/3 foot 4 inches tall

Typical characteristics:
Tangly leaves, tubular
in shape

Cultivation:
Full sun; light, rich soil
not compacted; water
during dry spells; plant
out the cloves in rows in
the spring at decent
intervals; undemanding

This plant of the leek family, characterised as much by a pungent smell as by its pleasant flavour, can look back on centuries of being used as a seasoning and medicinal herb. It is very well known for its antiseptic, expectorant, diaphoretic and hypotensive properties. It is also reputed to reduce blood sugar levels and act as an anticoagulant.

• Recipes pp. 91, 94, 95, 96, 101, 103, 104, 105, 109

Allium schoenoprasum – Chives

Family:
Alliaceae (leek family)

Also known as:
Chive

Range:
Europe and Asia

Size:
Perennial growing up to
30 cm/1 foot tall

Typical characteristics:
Aromatic leaves and
dense inflorescent violet
flowers

Cultivation:
Sunny to partial shade;
rich, limy soil; keep moist;
sow outdoors from
March onwards

Rich in vitamins, chives are very versatile. They can often be found in salads, vegetable and egg dishes, stews, meat and fish dishes or scrambled eggs as well as finely chopped on buttered bread or as a decorative ingredient for soups. The leaves, however, are also said to have appetising and stomachic properties.

• Recipe p. 92

Allium ursinum – Ramsons

Family:
Alliaceae (leek family)

Also known as:
Buckrams, bear's or wood
garlic

Range:
Europe

Size:
Perennial growing up to
50 cm/1 foot 8 inches tall

Typical characteristics:
The leaves have a strong
garlic odour

Cultivation:
Partial shade to shade;
moist, rich soil; plant
out bulbs in the autumn
or sow seeds from
August onwards

Ramsons or wild garlic is a favourite in the kitchen because its taste is reminiscent of garlic, yet milder and does not cause unwelcome bad breath or body odour. Naturopathy uses both bulbs and those parts of the plant exposed to daylight to alleviate symptoms of an upset stomach, flatulence and colic. It is also known to have appetising effects and stimulate the gastrointestinal tract.

• Recipe p. 83

Anethum graveolens – Dill

Family:
Apiaceae/Umbelliferaceae
(parsley family)

Also known as:
Dillweed

Range:
Asia

Size:
Annual plant growing up
to 75 cm/2 ½ foot tall

Typical characteristics:
Aromatic plant with hol-
low stems

Cultivation:
Full sun, protected from
the wind; light soil rich in
humus; water during dry
periods, aerate ground
occasionally; sow out-
doors from April onwards

Already the ancient Egyptians during the times of the Pharaos knew of dill as a painkiller, while the ancient Greeks placed the herb on their eyes to help them sleep. Dill in the kitchen is used to give soups, sauces as well as fish and meat that extra touch. Mature seeds may be used as a substitute for caraway seeds.

• Application p. 117; • Recipe pp. 68, 72, 109

Anthriscus cerefolium – Chervil

Family:
Apiaceae/Umbelliferaceae
(parsley family)

Also known as:
French parsley

Range:
Southern Europe, Asia
and North Africa

Size:
Annual plant growing up
to 60 cm/2 foot tall

Typical characteristics:
Leaves with a mild
aromatic flavour,
suggestive of aniseed

Cultivation:
Partial shade; prefers a
well drained moisture
retentive soil; water during dry periods; sow out-
doors from March/April
onwards, self-sowing

Chervil is a very old medicinal and culinary herb whose seeds were already found in Tutankhamen's tomb. In the kitchen, the leaves are a favourite to flavour soups and sauces, fish, lamb, curd cheese and egg dishes. In addition, chervil juice is a therapeutic treatment for skin ailments such as eczema and abscesses.

• Recipe pp. 88, 92

Arnica montana – Arnica

Family:
Asteraceae/Compositae
(daisy family)

Also known as:
Leopard's bane, mountain
tobacco, wolf's bane

Range:
Europe

Size:
Perennial growing up to
60 cm/2 foot tall

Typical characteristics:
Large flower heads with
long daisy like flowers

Cultivation:
Full sun; sandy, acidic,
peaty soil rich in humus;
do not fertilise;
to propagate divide
rhizome or sow out

In the old days, this medicinal herb was a must for every medicine cabinet as drugs made from it have antiseptic, anti-rheumatic and anti-arthritic properties among others. Because of some poisonous substances which necessitate precise dosage, both root and flowers are only applied externally, for example as an ointment for sprains and muscle pains.

• Application p. 119

Artemisia absinthium – Wormwood

Family:
Asteraceae/Compositae
(daisy family)

Also known as:
Green ginger, madderwort

Range:
Europe

Size:
Perennial growing up to
1 m/3 foot 4 inches tall

Typical characteristics:
Very hairy leaves, strong
aromatic odour

Cultivation:
Full sun; light, dry and
well drained soil;
propagation through
division of the plant or
cuttings; undemanding

This plant is not only the source for an often used flavouring agent for alcoholic drinks, but also a much sought after medicinal herb. It is mainly used to stimulate the digestive tract because it contains substances that boost the production of gastric acid. In the olden days, leaves and stalks were used against worms and insects.

• Application p. 117

• Recipe p. 73

Artemisia dracunculus – Tarragon

Family:
Asteraceae/Compositae
(daisy family)

Also known as:
Biting dragon, dragon
plant, estragon

Range:
Southern Russia and
Central Asia

Size:
Perennial growing up to
1 m/3 foot 4 inches tall

Typical characteristics:
The plant has a very
aromatic odour

Cultivation:
Sunny to partial shade,
warm; moist soil rich
in humus; water well
during dry spells

This plant was first mentioned in 3,000 year old Chinese scriptures. Since then, it has not lost any of its popularity because of its appetising and digestive properties. In the kitchen, tarragon leaves are also used to enhance soups, sauces, curd cheese dishes, salads and to season meat and poultry dishes.

• Recipe pp. 68, 70, 92, 100

Artemisia vulgaris – Mugwort

Family:
Asteraceae/Compositae
(daisy family)

Also known as:
Common mugwort,
common wormwood

Range:
Europe, Asia and
North Africa

Size:
Perennial growing up to
1.5 m/5 foot tall

Typical characteristics:
Leaves with dense white
tomentose hairs on the
underside

Cultivation:
Sunny; dry, poor soil;
undemanding; sow out in
the spring; propagation
also possible by division

For the sake of their feet and soles, Roman soldiers used mugwort leaves to line their *caligae* (military sandals). These days the herb is known mainly for of its aromatic, appetising, digestive and calming properties. In the kitchen, mugwort is used to season meat dishes.

Borago officinalis – Borage

Family:
Boraginaceae
(borage family)

Also known as:
Starflower, burrage

Range:
Europe

Size:
Annual plant growing up
to 60 cm/2 foot tall

Typical characteristics:
The prominent stamen have
connated to a purple cone

Cultivation:
Sunny to partial shade;
well drained soil rich in
humus; keep moist; sow out
from April to June, seeds
must be raked in; self-sower

From ancient times to the Middle Ages borage was regarded as a remedy against melancholia and sadness. These days, its leaves are much valued for their diuretic, anti-rheumatic, diaphoretic and anti-inflammatory properties. They also increase the flow of sputum. In the kitchen, the plant is sometimes used for salads and sauces.

• Recipe p. 68

Brassica juncea – Brown Mustard

Family:
Brassicaceae
(cabbage family)

Also known as:
Indian mustard, green
mustard

Range:
Europe and Asia

Size:
Annual plant growing up
to 1 m/3 foot 4 inches tall

Typical characteristics:
Long pods emanating
from the stem

Cultivation:
Sunny to protected with
no shade; rich,
well drained soil;
sow out from the middle
of March onwards; can be
used as green manure

Because brown mustard is very suitable to machine harvesting, it has replaced its close relative the black mustard (*brassica negra*) as the main source for the industrial manufacture of mustard. However, the seeds can also be used as a mild painkiller or a diuretic while its tasty leaves complement every salad or go well with bread and butter.

Calendula officinalis – Marigold

Family:
Asteraceae/Compositae
(daisy family)

Also known as:
Mary growles, ruddes,
golds

Range:
Southern Europe

Size:
Annual plant growing up
to 60 cm/2 foot tall

Typical characteristics:
Large, bright orange
coloured flowers

Cultivation:
Full sun; fresh, medium
heavy soil; water during
prolonged periods of
drought; sow out from
March onwards

Because of its anti-inflammatory and skin-healing properties, Marigold is used mostly for cuts and lacerations, abrasions, burns and other small injuries or lesions. Flower bearing shoots and leaves can also treat sunburn and skin rashes. The plant is also said to have astringent, antiseptic and detoxicating properties.

• Application p. 118

Carum carvi – Caraway

Family:
Apiaceae/Umbelliferaceae
(parsley family)

Also known as:
Caraway seed

Range:
Europe, Asia and North
Africa

Size:
Biannual plant growing
up to 60 cm/2 foot tall

Typical characteristics:
Furrowed, striat stalk,
deeply divided, finely cut
leaves

Cultivation:
Full sun; moist, rich soil
with lots of humus; water
during dry spells; sow out
from April onwards

Caraway, which has been found at excavations of 5,000 year-old pile dwellings, continues to be a popular seasoning to this day. The culinary uses of the caraway seeds include, but are not limited to, adding that little bit of spice to cabbage, sauerkraut, stews, meat and curd cheese dishes as well as breads and spirits. They also have antispasmodic and antiseptic properties.

Coriandrum sativum – Coriander

Family:
Apiaceae/Umbelliferaceae
(parsley family)

Also known as:
Chinese parsley, cilantro

Range:
Southern Europe and the
Middle East

Size:
Annual plant growing up
to 60 cm/2 foot tall

Typical characteristics:
Older plants give off an
unpleasant odour

Cultivation:
Full sun; light, slightly
alkaline soil; sow out
from April onwards
leaving each seedling
enough space; unde-
manding

The leaves of this wort serve to season salads and sauces as well as venison and fish dishes. They can also be used in baking and preserving. An infusion of the seeds encourages the workings of the digestive tract and helps in case of flatulence, unpleasant feeling of fullness or an upset stomach. Chewing the seeds after having eaten a lot of garlic is said to rid off bad breath.

• Recipe pp. 80, 84, 106

Cymbopogon citratus – Lemon Grass

Family:
Poaceae
(grass family)

Also known as:
Oil grass

Range:
Southeast Asia

Size:
Up to 1.5 m/5 foot tall
grass growing into dense
clumps

Typical characteristics:
Gives off an intense
lemony aroma

Cultivation:
Full sun; needs at least
13 °C/55 °F throughout
the year; moist, rich soil;
propagation through
division; delicate plant

This plant, which is only known in its cultivated form, is a favourite in Asian cooking and lends the extra bit of spice to lamb, pork, beef and poultry dishes. A tea made from lemon grass helps in case of indigestion as its antispasmodic ingredients relax the digestive tract. Moreover, it can be applied externally in cases such as small aches and pains.

• Recipe pp. 101, 107

Eruca sativa – Rocket

Family:
Brassicaceae
(cabbage family)

Also known as:
Aurrugula

Range:
Southern Europe

Size:
Annual plant growing up to
50 cm/1 foot 8 inches tall

Typical characteristics:
White to light yellow flowers with purple veins

Cultivation:
Sunny to partial shade;
light soil rich in humus;
water during dry spells
but avoid prolonged
periods of stagnant water;
sow out from April
onwards; undemanding

In the Middle Ages, rocket was
a favourite seasoning because of its strong flavour – a time
when solid meals were the order of the day. These days the
herb, its flavour reminiscent of watercress, is used in salads
or on bread and butter. Apart from its culinary qualities, it also
contains agents with appetising properties. It acts as a tonic,
cleans the blood and is rich in vitamins A and C.

• Recipe p. 86

Filipendula ulmaria – Meadowsweet

Family:
Rosaceae
(rose family)

Also known as:
Bridewort, dropwort

Range:
Europe

Size:
Perennial growing up to
1.5 m/5 foot tall

Typical characteristics:
Long, yellow flower
panicles

Cultivation:
Sunny to partial shade;
loamy, rich and moist soil;
water well during dry
periods; avoid prolonged
periods of stagnant water;
mulch in the spring

Meadowsweet was one of three holy plants of the Celtic
druids. Its name stems from the fact that it was used as a
sweetener for mead. Naturotherapy knows of the wort's
painkilling and anti-inflammatory properties; shoots in
bloom are also often used in case of indigestion.

Foeniculum vulgare var. Dulce – Sweet Fennel

Family:
Apiaceae/Umbelliferaceae
(parsley family)

Also known as:
Florence fennel, anise

Range:
Mediterranean and
Western Asia

Size:
Perennial growing up to
1.5 m/5 foot tall

Typical characteristics:
Wort with a very strong
aroma

Cultivation:
Full sun; chalky soil rich
in humus; keep moist;
cut back to 8 cm/3 inches
above the ground in
the autumn

This particular variety of fennel produces very aromatic and slightly sweet seeds, making them an ideal seasoning. The long leaves are also perfect for salads. All varieties of fennel have aromatic, appetising, diuretic and antispasmodic properties. They are also excellent against flatulence and stimulate the digestive tract.

• Application p. 117

Galium odoratum – Woodruff

Family:
Rubiaceae
(madder family)

Also known as:
Sweetscented bedstraw,
our Lady's lace

Range:
Europe and
Southwest Asia

Size:
Perennial growing up to
30 cm/1 foot tall

Typical characteristics:
Leaves arranged in a
whorl, aromatic odour

Cultivation:
Partial shade to full
shade; rich soil; propagation through division or
layering off-shoots

In Germany, woodruff is an indispensable ingredient in may wine, a white wine punch. It is also often used to flavour ice-cream or syrup. It is used, for example, in a weak German wheat beer called "Berliner Weisse." Stalks and leaves can be made into an herbal tea that has appetising, antispasmodic and calming properties. It also stimulates the digestive tract.

• Recipe p. 73

Helichrysum italicum ssp. Serotinum – Curry Plant

Family:
Asteraceae/Compositae
(daisy family)

Also known as:
Everlasting flower

Range:
Southern Europe

Size:
Perennial growing up to
45 cm/1 ½ foot tall

Typical characteristics:
Leaves give off a strong
curry odour

Cultivation:
Full sun, protected; well
drained, rather dry, poor
soil; plant out greenhouse
plants from May on-
wards; remove whithered
parts of the plant

This wort is not a relative of the curry leaf tree (Murraya koenigii) hailing from India and the Himalaya region, which is the main ingredient of the curry powder we all know. Its aromatic leaves are ideally suited to give soups, stews or vegetable and rice dishes a hint of curry.

Humulus lupulus – Hops

Family:
Cannabaceae
(hemp family)

Also known as:
Common hop, humulus

Range:
Europe and Asia

Size:
Climber growing up to
7 m/25 foot tall

Typical characteristics:
Female seed heads grow
cone like shapes

Cultivation:
Prefers sun; soil rich in
humus; water liberally;
requires climbing aids;
plant out from middle
of May onwards

Hops do not only play an important role in the brewing industry, but has long been acknowledged to be effective against sleepless nights in the form of hop pillows which give off a mild aroma, hop tea or hop pills. The plant is also good for digestion and colic. The female seed heads are used.

Hypericum perforatum – St. John's Wort

Family:
Clusiaceae/Hypericaceae
(mamey family)

Also known as:
Goat weed, klamath weed,
tipton weed

Range:
Europe

Size:
Perennial growing up to
80 cm/2 foot 8 inches tall

Typical characteristics:
Oval seed pod that
separates into three
when opening up

Cultivation:
Sunny, protected; slightly
moist soil; requires winter
protection when on exposed
sites; severe cutting back

Because its flowering period coincides with the summer solstice, St. John's Wort was regarded a magical plant which was said to protect against bad luck. These days, it is one of the most commonly used preparations against nervous disorders such as anxiety attacks, sleeplessness and depression. The plant is also thought to alleviate problems caused by menopause. Usually, the tips of flowering shoots are used.

Hyssopus officinalis – Hyssop

Family:
Lamiaceae/Labiatae
(mint family)

Also known as:
–

Range:
Southern Europe and
Southwest Asia

Size:
Perennial growing up to
60 cm/2 foot tall

Typical characteristics:
Leaves give off an
aromatic odour

Cultivation:
Full sun; well drained,
chalky soil; best to plant
in the spring; during
the winter protect
with brushwood

Hyssop may only be ingested or applied under proper medical observation. It is known to calm the digestive tract in case of flatulence, an unpleasant feeling of fullness or colic. Inflorescences and essential oils are also used in case of bronchitis and other infections of the airways with excessive excretion of mucus. It is also used to treat throat or teeth inflammation.

• Recipe p. 69

Juniperus communis – Juniper

Family:
Cupressaceae
(cypress family)

Also known as:
Common juniper

Range:
Europe, Asia and North
America

Size:
Up to 15 m/50 foot tall,
dioecious plant (only one
sex on any one plant)

Typical characteristics:
Coniferous leaves and
round, blue frosted fruit

Cultivation:
Full sun; all soils;
undemanding;
do not cut back

In former times, juniper branches were thrown into the fire as a protection against bad spirits. Nowadays, things have changed somewhat and juniper berries are used as an accompaniment for venison and other meat dishes. In naturotherapy, it is used for its diuretic and antiseptic properties. Juniper should be avoided during pregnancy.

• Recipe p. 104

Laurus nobilis – Bay Tree

Family:
Lauraceae
(laurel family)

Also known as:
Bay laurel, sweet laurel

Range:
Mediterranean

Size:
Evergreen shrub or tree
growing up to
20 m/65 foot tall

Typical characteristics:
Leaves give off an
aromatic odour

Cultivation:
Sunny, warm; fertile soil
rich in humus; keep
moisture content even;
place in a bright spot
during the winter at
about 5 °C/41 °F

The bay tree has aromatic and appetising properties and stimulates the digestive tract. It not only has mild antiseptic and anti-rheumatic properties, but can also be used as a painkiller. In the kitchen, its leaves add something to every meat dish, soup or sauce and lend vinegar a special touch.

• Recipe pp. 68, 72, 89, 95

Lavandula angustifolia – Common Lavender

Family:
Lamiaceae/Labiatae
(mint family)

Also known as:
English lavender, lavender

Range:
Mediterranean

Size:
Bush growing up to 80 cm/
2 foot 8 inches in height

Typical characteristics:
Lance like leaves and very
aromatic flowers

Cultivation:
Full sun, warm; permeable
soil, preferably a little
on the dry side; cut all
shoots down by a third in
the spring; protect with
brushwood during the
winter months

Even though the aromatic lavender is grown on a large scale for the manufacture of perfumes and cosmetics, it is a much valued ingredient in sauces, soups, stews, fish and minced meat dishes. It is said to have antiseptic, sedative, anti-depressive and antispasmodic properties.

• Application p. 124;

• Recipe pp. 70, 71, 73

Lepidium sativum – Garden Cress

Family:
Brassicaceae
(cabbage family)

Also known as:
Pepperweed, pepper grass

Range:
Central Asia

Size:
Annual plant growing up to
40 cm/1 foot 4 inches tall

Typical characteristics:
Lower leaves elongated
and egg shaped;
upper leaves deeply
divided and finely cut

Cultivation:
Sunny to partial shade;
fresh to moist soil;
keep moist at all times;
sow out evenly from
March onwards

Rich in vitamins, savoury cress is a favourite with bread and butter, salads, curd cheese and egg dishes or sauces. Because of its unique and wonderful taste it was already treasured by the ancient Greeks and Romans. It probably conquered central Europe around the time of Charles the Great (747–814).

• Recipe p. 88

Levisticum officinale – Lovage

Family:
Apiaceae/Umbelliferaceae
(parsley family)

Also known as:
Love parsley, wild celery

Range:
Southern Europe and
Southwest Asia

Size:
Perennial plant growing
up to 2 m/7 foot in height

Typical characteristics:
Tall, cylindrical stalk

Cultivation:
Sunny to partial shade;
fertile soil; water during
dry periods; fertilise
on an annual basis;
undemanding

Lovage has always been a favourite in the kitchen. In Germany, its common name even refers to a famous liquid seasoning. It is ideal for fish and meat dishes and lends mayonnaise or herb butter a special touch. Naturotherapy has it that its fruit and root help in case of problems with the digestive system, loss of appetite, bronchitis and urinary tract infection.

• Recipe pp. 72, 98

Matricaria recutita – German Camomile

Family:
Asteraceae/Compositae
(daisy family)

Also known as:
Scented mayweed,
chamomile

Range:
Europe

Size:
Annual plant growing up
to 60 cm/2 foot in height

Typical characteristics:
Yellow disk flowers
surrounded by white
ray-shaped petals

Cultivation:
Full sun, warm; soil rich
in humus; sow out evenly
from April onwards;
separate afterwards;
totally undemanding

German camomile is one of the most valuable medicinal herbs. The dried flower heads can be used for digestive problems and as a vulnerary agent. They also have anti-inflammatory properties and a calming effect. Their antispasmodic effects can help ease menstruation pain.

• Application p. 122;
• Recipe pp. 70, 71, 73

Melissa officinalis – Lemon Balm

Family:
Lamiaceae/Labiatae
(mint family)

Also known as:
Sweet balm, common
balm, bee herb

Range:
Mediterranean and
Western Asia

Size:
Perennial plant growing
up to 1.5 m/5 foot
in height

Typical characteristics:
Both a lemony odour
and taste

Cultivation:
Sunny to partial shade;
protected; soil rich in
humus; requires cutting
back; undemanding

Lemon balm may be a favourite for bees (the Greek word "melissa" means bee), but humans also value it for its aromatic, calming, antispasmodic and diaphoretic properties. This medicinal herb stimulates the digestive tract. Its culinary uses include, but are not confined to, seasoning salads, sauces, fish, meat and poultry dishes. The best parts of the plant are the leaves and flowering shoots.

• Application pp. 117, 123;

• Recipe pp. 68, 70, 71, 73, 110

Mentha x piperita – Peppermint

Family:
Lamiaceae/Labiatae
(mint family)

Also known as:
Black peppermint, choco-
late mint, orange mint

Range:
–

Size:
Perennial plant growing
up to 80 cm/2 foot
8 inches in height

Typical characteristics:
Specially strong odour

Cultivation:
Sunny to partial shade;
light, moist soil;
water during dry spells;
keep under control by
cutting off offsets

Peppermint is a cross between the spearmint (*Mentha spicata*) and water mint (*Mentha aquatica*) plants. In central Europe, it is mainly found cultivated in gardens and only rarely found in the wild. In the kitchen, its leaves and flowers make a refreshing tea. It is valued in naturotherapy because of its carminative, appetising, antiseptic, diaphoretic and anodyne properties.

• Application pp. 117;

• Recipe pp. 68–71, 73, 81, 85, 88, 93

Mentha x rotundifolia – Apple Mint

Family:
Lamiaceae/Labiatae
(mint family)

Also known as:
Round leaved mint,
Egyptian mint

Range:
Cross between M. longi-
folia and M. suaveolens

Size:
Perennial plant growing
up to 60 cm/2 foot
in height

Typical characteristics:
Hairy leaves reminiscent
of apple trees

Cultivation:
Sunny to partial shade;
light, moist soil rich
in humus; can be cut
right back

The leaves and leaf stalks of apple mint can not only make a fruity aromatic tea, but are also used in salads or to season meat dishes. The plant has therapeutic uses because it contains active ingredients against flatulence and fever. It also has antiseptic properties. It should be avoided during pregnancy.

Nepeta cataria – Catnip

Family:
Lamiaceae/Labiatae
(mint family)

Also known as:
Cat mint

Range:
Southeastern Europe
and Western Asia

Size:
Perennial plant growing
up to 1 m/3 foot 4 inches
in height

Typical characteristics:
Gives off a strong, mint-
like odour

Cultivation:
Full sun to partial shade;
permeable to dry soil;
totally undemanding;
cut back after flowering

This plant owes its name to the fact that cats find its strong odour nigh irresistible. Naturotherapy uses the worty parts of the plant in case of flatulence and colics, sometimes even for headaches caused by indigestion. Catnip is said to have aromatic, appetising, antispasmodic, diaphoretic as well as sedative properties.

143

Ocimum basilicum – Basil

Family:
Lamiaceae/Labiatae
(mint family)

Also known as:
Sweet basil,
St. Joseph's wort

Range:
India

Size:
Annual plant growing up
to 50 cm/1 foot 8 inches
in height

Typical characteristics:
Tetragonal stalk and
white flowers

Cultivation:
Full sun, warm; fertile,
light soil; keep moisture
level constant; if necessary
apply organic fertiliser

Basil's culinary uses are well known and extend to season meat and fish dishes as well as stews. Naturotherapy makes use of its leaves' and flowers' calming properties to counteract problems with the digestive tract or nervous system. It is, therefore, a favourite in case of nausea and vomiting or sleeping problems, nervousness or increased states of anxiety.

• Recipe pp. 68, 69, 70, 73, 82, 94, 98

Origanum majorana – Marjoram

Family:
Lamiaceae/Labiatae
(mint family)

Also known as:
Sweet marjoram,
knotted marjoram

Range:
Probably Southwest or
Central Asia

Size:
Bush growing up to 50 cm/
1 foot 8 inches in height

Typical characteristics:
Because of their silky
hairs, young leaves can
appear to be white

Cultivation:
Full sun, warm; light,
alkaline soil rich in humus;
water during dry periods

Marjoram's uses as a culinary herb include the seasoning of roast lamb, mutton, beef and pork as well as of fish and poultry dishes. It also plays an important role in the manufacturing of sausages. It has antispasmodic, anti-neuralgic and sedative properties. It also stimulates the digestive tract. Marjoram should be avoided during pregnancy.

• Application p. 117

Origanum vulgare – Oregano

Family:
Lamiaceae/Labiatae
(mint family)

Also known as:
Wild marjoram,
Greek oregano

Range:
Europe and
Southwest Asia

Size:
Perennial plant growing
up to 80 cm/2 foot 8
inches in height

Typical characteristics:
Reddish stalks and
hairy leaves

Cultivation:
Full sun, warm; dry and
poor soil; undemanding;
cut back to the ground
in the spring

Oregano is a favourite seasoning for pizzas and pasta dishes, but also goes well with a variety of fish and meat dishes. Naturotherapy values especially its aromatic, appetising, antispasmodic, antiseptic and cholagogue properties. It stimulates the digestive tract and acts as a mild stimulant. Parts of the plant used include the tips of flowering shoots.

• Recipe pp. 68, 87

Petroselinum crispum var. Crispum – Double Curled Parsley

Family:
Apiaceae/Umbelliferaceae
(parsley family)

Also known as:
French parsley,
Italian parsley,
plain-leaved parsley

Range:
Mediterranean

Size:
Bi-annual plant growing
up to 60 cm/2 foot
in height

Typical characteristics:
Very curly leaves

Cultivation:
Sunny to partial shade;
fresh, light soil; keep
moist; fertilise using
mature compost; cover
over the winter months

In Egypt, during the time of the Pharaohs this wort must have played an important role in the death cult for it was often found in tombs bound to a wreath. These days, there are many different varieties with differently shaped leaves (this variety has curly edges) or roots.

• Recipe pp. 72, 89, 98, 100, 103

Petroselinum crispum var. neapolitanum – Flat Leaf Parsley

Family:
Apiaceae/Umbelliferaceae
(parsley family)

Also known as:
Italian parsley

Range:
Mediterranean

Size:
Bi-annual plant growing
up to 60 cm/2 foot
in height

Typical characteristics:
Flat, even leaves

Cultivation:
Sunny to partial shade;
permeable, fertile soil
rich in humus; sow out
from the middle of
March onwards

This variety with its smooth leaves has a somewhat stronger taste than its close relative the double curly leaved parsley (*Petroselinum crispum* var. *crispum*). Both varieties are very rich in vitamins and minerals which is probably part of the reason why they are popular in salads, sauces, soups, curd cheese dishes, mayonnaise, potato and fish dishes. They also make for an attractive decoration.

• Recipe pp. 93, 103, 105

Pimpinella anisum – Anise

Family:
Apiaceae/Umbelliferaceae
(parsley family)

Also known as:
Anason, anasur, anisu

Range:
Mediterranean

Size:
Annual plant growing up
to 60 cm/2 foot in height

Typical characteristics:
Gives off an aromatic
odour; bristly fruit

Cultivation:
Full sun, warm;
permeable alkaline soil;
water during dry periods;
sow out from
April onwards

This plants' seeds are commonly used as a seasoning for meat dishes, salads, vegetables, sauces and in baking. Moreover, because the wort has calming properties, the ancient Egyptians already valued it as a medicinal herb. Even these days, anise seeds are well known for their antispasmodic properties and are often prescribed against menstrual pain. They are also used against an unpleasant feeling of fullness and flatulence.

Rosmarinus officinalis – Rosemary

Family:
Lamiaceae/Labiatae
(mint family)

Also known as:
Wild rosemary

Range:
Mediterranean

Size:
Evergreen bush growing up
to 2 m/7 foot in height

Typical characteristics:
Pine needle like leaves
with dense fine hairs
below

Cultivation:
Full sun, warm; permeable,
poor soil; do not fertilise;
water a little during
prolonged dry spells

Young rosemary shoots have many culinary uses and serve as a seasoning for poultry, lamb, venison, rabbit and pork as well for pizza, soups and vegetables. However, the wort has multifaceted uses in that it also boasts stimulating, aromatic, antispasmodic, tonic, astringent, diuretic, anti-inflammatory and carminative effects. Rosemary is said to stimulate the digestive track.

• Application p. 117;

• Recipe pp. 69–73, 91, 102, 104

Rumex acetosa – Common Sorrel

Family:
Polygonaceae
(buckwheat family)

Also known as:
Garden sorrel, sour dock

Range:
Europe and Asia

Size:
Perennial plant growing
up to 1 m/3 foot 4 inches
in height

Typical characteristics:
Angular stalks with a
reddish taint and
elongated oval leaves

Cultivation:
Sunny to shady;
moist soil rich in humus;
keep moist at all times;
remove flower buds as
soon as they appear

Even though, as early as the 12th century, the famous herbalist and abbess Hildegard of Bingen said of common sorrel that it would only be of use to cattle rather than humans, these days the plant is said to have diuretic, anti-inflammatory, refreshing, cleansing, febrifuge and mild laxative properties. All the parts of the plant that are exposed to sunlight may be used.

• Recipe p. 88

Ruta graveolens – Rue

Family:
Rutaceae
(citrus family)

Also known as:
Herb of grace
or repentance

Range:
Mediterranean

Size:
Perennial plant growing
up to 1 m/3 foot 4 inches
in height

Typical characteristics:
Bluish-green, fleshy leaves
with numerous oily glands

Cultivation:
Full sun; warm;
light and moist infertile
soil; propagation through
division or layering

Although rue is poisonous when taken in large doses, it has appetising, antispasmodic, diuretic and calming properties. It also stimulates the digestive tract. Consumption should, however, be under medical supervision. In the kitchen, it serves to season meat and fish dishes. It is also used to flavour liqueurs such as the Italian grappa.

Salvia officinalis – Common Sage

Family:
Lamiaceae/Labiatae
(mint family)

Also known as:
Kitchen sage, garden sage

Range:
Mediterranean

Size:
Evergreen bush growing
up to 80 cm/2 foot
8 inches in height

Typical characteristics:
Thick, woolly, elongated,
elliptical leaves

Cultivation:
Full sun, warm;
permeable, reasonably
dry and rather poor soil;
undemanding

Culinary uses of common sage include the seasoning of veal, beef and pork and the flavouring of herbal oil and vinegar. As a medicinal herb, it is valued because of its antiseptic, anti-inflammatory, carminative, cholagogue and diaphoretic properties. It also acts as a tonic and stimulates the digestive tract.

• Application p. 116;

• Recipe pp. 68, 69, 73, 96, 99, 100

Salvia sclarea – Clary

Family:
Lamiaceae/Labiatae
(mint family)

Also known as:
Clary sage

Range:
Europe, Asia

Size:
Bi-annual plant growing
up to 1.2 m/4 foot
in height

Typical characteristics:
Very small,
egg-shaped oval leaves

Cultivation:
Full sun, warm; perme-
able, reasonably dry and
poor soil; undemanding;
cut back when the plant
grows too big

The aromatic clary is often used in the food industry, especially in flavouring liqueurs and vermouth. This herb is responsible for the pleasant aroma reminiscent of the
muscadet grape and the digestive properties of such drinks.
The tips of the flowering shoots are also said to have appetising and antispasmodic properties.

Sambucus nigra – Common Elder

Family:
Caprifoliaceae
(honeysuckle family)

Also known as:
Pipe tree, bore tree,
black elder

Range:
Europe

Size:
Tall shrub or small tree
growing up to 10 m/
35 foot in height

Typical characteristics:
Egg-shaped, serrated
leaves, black berries

Cultivation:
Full range from sun to
shade; happy in all
but moist soils; sunny
to shady; prune every
2–3 years; undemanding

Common elder flowers are well known for their relaxing,
febrifuge and diaphoretic properties which makes them a
favourite against the effects of colds. The flowers are also
used against rheumatic and neuralgic complaints. Elder
berries are very rich in vitamin C, have slight laxative properties and can be used as a colouring agent.

Sanguisorba minor – Salad Burnet

Family:
Rosaceae
(rose family)

Also known as:
Small burnet,
garden burnet

Range:
Europe

Size:
Perennial plant growing
up to 60 cm/2 foot
in height

Typical characteristics:
Greenish or purple
inflorescences

Cultivation:
Full sun; dry, chalky, light
soil; water during
prolonged dry periods;
remove inflorescences
at an early stage

In Europe, salad burnet is used both as a fodder plant and to brew beer. It has aromatic, appetising, and astringent properties. Because it stimulates the digestive tract, it is ideal for loss of appetite and an upset stomach. It can even be used to treat minor burns. The whole plant apart from the root may be used.

• Recipe p. 71, 72

Satureja hortensis – Summer Savory

Family:
Lamiaceae/Labiatae
(mint family)

Also known as:
–

Range:
Mediterranean

Size:
Annual plant growing up
to 40 cm/1 foot 4 inches
in height

Typical characteristics:
Worty, very aromatic
plant, gives off a
strong odour

Cultivation:
Full sun, warm; soil rich
in humus; cover with a
fleece during cold spells;
sow out from
May onwards

This wort is an old favourite for flavouring beans. It is also used as a seasoning for meat dishes, stocks or for pickling gherkins. It has antispasmodic and stimulant properties, especially of the digestive tract. A footbath is said to have a pleasant and deoderising effect on stressed feet.

• Recipe p. 69

Satureja montana – Winter Savory

Family:
Lamiaceae/Labiatae
(mint family)

Also known as:
Creeping savory

Range:
Mediterranean

Size:
Shrub growing up to
40 cm/1 foot 4 inches
in height

Typical characteristics:
Woody plant giving off a
strong aromatic odour

Cultivation:
Full sun, warm;
permeable, rather poor,
dryish soil; cut back
slightly in the spring

Already, ancient physicians used this plant for its therapeutic effects both as an antiseptic agent and as a tonic. These days, winter savory is sometimes applied in case of flatulence or colic or for respiratory problems such as bronchitis. In the kitchen, it can be used in the same way as its close relative the summer savory (Satureja hortensis), i.e. for flavouring beans.

Symphytum officinale – Common Comfrey

Family:
Boraginaceae
(borage family)

Also known as:
Knitbone, boneset,
blackwort, gum plant

Range:
Europe, Africa and
North America

Size:
Perennial plant growing
up to 1 m/3 foot 4 inches
in height

Typical characteristics:
Leaves have numerous
glands

Cultivation:
Sunny to partial shade;
moist, fertile, loamy soil
rich in humus;
undemanding

The Latin name Symphytum means "to grow together". This is an indication that in ancient times the herb must have been used in the treatment of broken bones. Even these days, the plant is used to treat sprains. It is also found in lotions against acne, haemorrhoids, slight burns, varicose veins and psoriasis.

151

Taraxacum officinale – Dandelion

Family:
Asteraceae/Compositae
(daisy family)

Also known as:
Cankerweed, blowball,
pee in the bed

Range:
Europe and Western Asia

Size:
Perennial plant growing
up to 50 cm/1 foot
8 inches in height

Typical characteristics:
Bare, hollow stem bearing
the flower head, filled
with milky white sap

Cultivation:
Sunny, partial shade;
slightly moist, fertile soil;
undemanding

Dandelions have been used for hundreds of years to treat gall and liver problems, digestive disorders and to reduce fever. Young leaves make for a nice salad or can be used as vegetables. Its roots can be used to make a substitute drink for coffee. However, the milky white sap can cause very unpleasant skin irritation – especially in children.

• Recipe p. 73

Thymus x citriodorus – Lemon Thyme

Family:
Lamiaceae/Labiatae
(mint family)

Also known as:
Silver queen

Range:
Europe

Size:
Small shrub growing up
to 40 cm/1 foot 4 inches
in height

Typical characteristics:
Gives off a strong
lemony odour

Cultivation:
Full sun, warm;
permeable, reasonably
dry, sandy soil that is
slightly acidic; cut back
by a third after flowering;
undemanding

This crossing between common thyme (*Thymus vulgaris*) and large thyme (*Thymus pulegioides*) which also occurs naturally, gives off an unusually strong lemony odour. A fact that has made it a popular border plant for flower beds and garden paths. In addition, it is very useful for aromatic pillows or flower bouquets. It goes well with fish dishes, poultry stuffing and vegetables.

Thymus vulgaris – Common Thyme

Family:
Lamiaceae/Labiatae
(mint family)

Also known as:
Garden thyme, rubbed
thyme

Range:
Mediterranean

Size:
Small shrub growing up to
10 cm/4 inches in height

Typical characteristics:
Elongated leaves with
downward curling edges

Cultivation:
Full sun, warm;
permeable, reasonably dry
and slightly acidic soil;
cut back by a third
following flowering

Common thyme is not only a famous seasoning but also has therapeutic effects similar to mother of thyme (*Thymus serpyllum*). Its culinary uses extend to flavouring soups, sauces, roast lamb or beef, poultry, stews and of course pizza. It is said to get rid off moths if added to pot-pourri.

• Application pp. 116, 117;

• Recipe pp. 68–70, 72, 73, 89, 91, 95, 97, 104

Tropaeolum majus – Garden Nasturtium

Family:
Tropaeolaceae
(nasturtium family)

Also known as:
Indian cress

Range:
Peru

Size:
Annual plant with shoots
growing up to 3 m/
10 foot in length

Typical characteristics:
Trumpet shaped flowers
with long spur

Cultivation:
Sunny to partial shade;
light, fertile soil; keep
evenly moist throughout

In South America, nasturtiums have been used for their vulnerary, disinfectant and expectorant properties, especially in the case of respiratory problems and deficiency symptoms of both the skin and hair. In the kitchen, its spicy leaves, incredibly rich in vitamins, find their way into salads, sauces, curd cheese and egg dishes or cream cheese while the flowers are used as a garnish.

Tussilago farfara – Coltsfoot

Family:
Asteraceae/Compositae
(daisy family)

Also known as:
Assfoot, clayweed,
coughwort

Range:
Europe and Asia

Size:
Perennial plant growing
up to 20 cm/8 inches
in height

Typical characteristics:
Flowers appear prior to
the leaves

Cultivation:
Full sun; poor, dry soil;
keep moist during spring;
keep under control
by removing offsets;
totally undemanding

Until recently, coltsfoot was a popular medicine against respiratory problems. In the kitchen, it is used in salads and soups or as a topping for bread and butter. Research has shown, however, that the plant contains harmful pyrrolizidine alkaloids and should therefore not be used.

Urtica dioica – Common Nettle

Family:
Urticaceae
(nettle family)

Also known as:
Stinging nettle,
big string nettle

Range:
Spread virtually
throughout the world

Size:
Perennial plant growing up
to 1.5 m/5 foot in height

Typical characteristics:
Covered in stinging hairs

Cultivation:
Sunny to partial shade;
loves soils rich in nitrate
and humus; propagation
either through sowing or
root division in spring

The common nettle is much valued for its detoxicating and cleansing effects. It is also said to have diuretic properties and alleviate a variety of skin ailments, very greasy hair, dandruff, and stop bleeding. Because of its anti-allergic properties, it is sometimes used against hay fever and asthma.

Valeriana officinalis – Valerian

Family:
Valerianaceae
(valerian family)

Also known as:
All-heal, set-well,
capon's tail

Range:
Europe and Northern Asia

Size:
Perennial plant growing up
to 1.2 m/4 foot in height

Typical characteristics:
Short, yellow to
brown rhizomes

Cultivation:
Sunny to partial shade;
moist soil rich in humus;
water during dry spells;
sow out during late
summer or autumn

During the Middle Ages, valerian was thought of as the near perfect medicine against any imaginable ailment including the black death, witches, the devil and evil spirits. These days the plant is valued for its relaxing qualities as it alleviates anxiety and stress. It is also often used in the form of a sleeping draught.

Verbascum densiflorum – Dense Flowered Mullein

Family:
Scrophulariaceae
(figwort family)

Also known as:
High taper, torch weed

Range:
Europe, Asia, Africa

Size:
Bi-annual plant growing
up to 2 m/7 foot
in height

Typical characteristics:
Indented leaves, yellow
leaves with a diameter
of approximately 4 cm/
2 inches

Cultivation:
Full sun; permeable,
fertile soil; propagation
by root division

This plant contains a great deal of fibrils, making it a favourite ingredient for cough mixtures, especially teas. It can also be used for rheumatic ailments or as a diuretic. External application includes treating wounds and use as a rub-on painkiller. The dense flowered mullein is also a colouring agent for natural fibres (yellow and green). Flowers, leaves and seeds may all be used.

Veronica beccabunga – Brooklime

Family:
Scrophulariaceae
(figwort family/
speedwell family)

Also known as:
Water pimpernel, cow
cress, limpwort

Range:
Europe, Asia, Africa

Size:
Perennial plant growing up
to 60 cm/2 foot in height

Typical characteristics:
Fleshy leaves, mostly blue
flowers

Cultivation:
Sun to partial shade; moist
to marshy soil, grows to
a water depth of 10 cm/
4 inches; undemanding

As its common name suggests, this central European species grows mainly on the shores of waterways. In the kitchen, its leaves can be made either into a salad or used as a vegetable. The therapeutic properties of its flowering shoots include an improved digestion and the cleansing of blood. They are also said to start menstruation.

Viola odorata – Sweet Violet

Family:
Violaceae
(violet family)

Also known as:
Ordinary violet, garden
violet

Range:
Europe and Asia

Size:
Perennial plant growing up
to 15 cm/½ foot in height

Typical characteristics:
Mainly blue to purple
flowers that give off a
pleasant aroma

Cultivation:
Partial shade to full shade;
slightly moist, fertile soil
rich in humus; undemand-
ing; propagation through
division or sowing seeds

Already in ancient times, sweet violet was used against an upset stomach and as an ingredient in cough mixtures. In the Middle Ages, this was extended to eye infections or skin ailments. But even these days, leaves and flowers of this established therapeutic plant are sometimes valued for their diuretic, expectorant, diaphoretic and laxative properties. It is also used in perfumes or flavourings.

Alphabetical Index